NUMBER® CORNER

SECOND EDITION
STUDENT BOOK

GRADE
2

Published by The **MATH LEARNING CENTER** *Salem, Oregon*

S0-BCX-679

Number Corner Second Edition Grade 2 Student Book

The Number Corner Grade 2 package consists of:

Number Corner Grade 2 Teachers Guide Volumes 1–3

Number Corner Grade 2 Teacher Masters

Number Corner Grade 2 Student Book

Number Corner Grade 2 Teacher Masters Answer Key

Number Corner Grade 2 Student Book Answer Key

Number Corner Grade 2 Components & Manipulatives

Assessment Guide:

• Number Corner Assessments

• Comprehensive Growth Assessment

Digital resources noted in italics.

The Math Learning Center, PO Box 12929, Salem, Oregon 97309. Tel 1 (800) 575-8130
www.mathlearningcenter.org

Prepared for publication using Mac OS X and Adobe Creative Suite.
Printed in the United States of America.

To reorder this book, refer to number 2NC2SB5 (package of 5).

QBN2901
06012020_LSC
Updated 2015-02-12.

Bridges in Mathematics is a standards-based K–5 curriculum that provides a unique blend of concept development and skills practice in the context of problem solving. It incorporates Number Corner, a collection of daily skill-building activities for students.

The Math Learning Center is a nonprofit organization serving the education community. Our mission is to inspire and enable individuals to discover and develop their mathematical confidence and ability. We offer innovative and standards-based professional development, curriculum, materials, and resources to support learning and teaching. To find out more, visit us at www.mathlearningcenter.org.

ISBN 978-1-60262-369-9

Number Corner Grade 2
Student Book

April

May

Sixty Minutes a Day, A.M. Record Sheet

12:00 Midnight

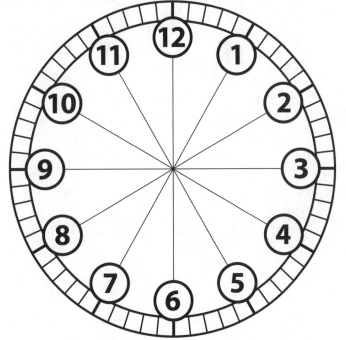

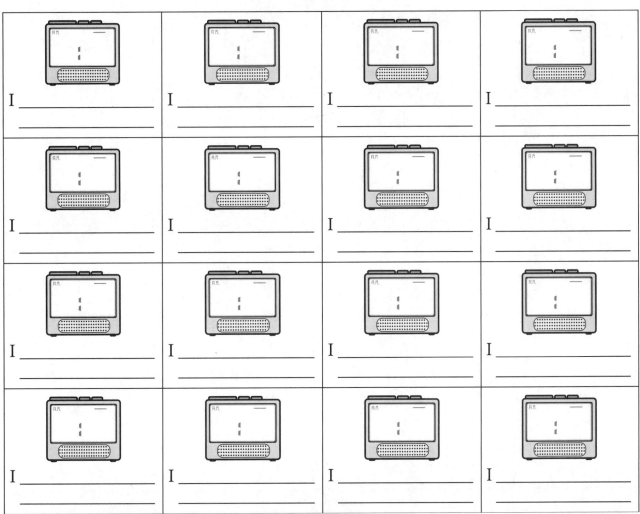

I _____

I _____

I _____

I _____

I _____

I _____

I _____

I _____

I _____

I _____

I _____

I _____

I _____

I _____

I _____

Sixty Minutes a Day, P.M. Record Sheet

12:00 Noon

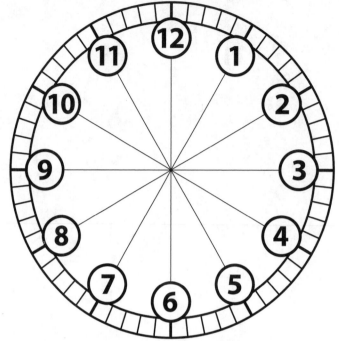

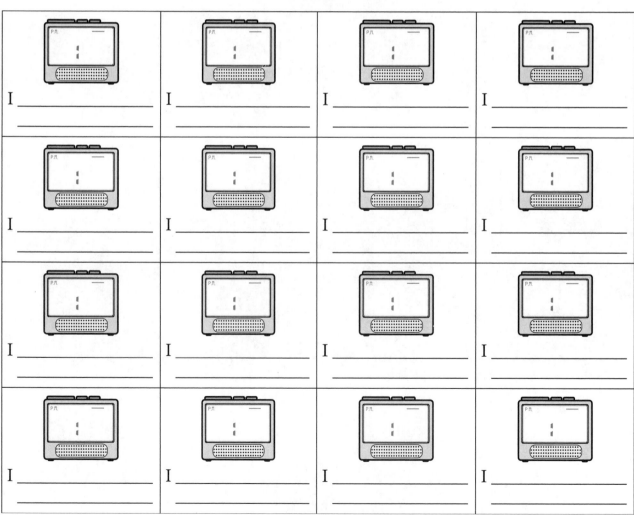

2

A.M. or P.M.? page 1 of 2

1 When do people usually do each of these things on a school day? Draw lines to **a.m.** or **p.m.** to show.

a.m.
Morning
(Between midnight and noon)

p.m.
Afternoon & Evening
(Between noon and midnight)

2 Marcus is in second grade. School starts for Marcus at (circle one):

8:15 a.m.   8:15 p.m.

3 Erica is in kindergarten. Erica eats dinner at (circle one):

6:00 a.m.   6:00 p.m.

4 James is 7 years old. James goes to bed at (circle one):

8:00 a.m.   8:00 p.m.

(continued on next page)

3

NAME _____ **| DATE** _____

A.M. or P.M.? page 2 of 2

5 Circle the time that people usually do each of these things on a school day.

a Eat lunch

12:00 noon   12:00 midnight

b Play at the park

3:00 a.m.   3:00 p.m.

c Go to basketball practice

4:30 a.m.   4:30 p.m.

6 Draw a picture of something you do in the a.m. and something you do in the p.m.

a.m.	**p.m.**

7 How many hours are there in a day? _____

Odd & Even Numbers

Write 1 addition and 1 subtraction equation for each even number. Write 2 addition and 2 subtraction equations for each odd number.

 6   Even   Odd   _____

 7   Even   Odd   _____

8   Even   Odd   _____

9   Even   Odd   _____

10   Even   Odd   _____

11   Even   Odd   _____

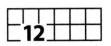 **12**   Even   Odd   _____

 **13**   Even   Odd   _____

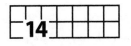 **14**   Even   Odd   _____

NAME _____ | DATE _____

Odd & Even Number Review page 1 of 2

1 Is 11 an odd or even number? How do you know? Use numbers, pictures, or words to explain your answer.

2 Is 12 an odd or even number? How do you know? Use numbers, pictures, or words to explain your answer.

3 Use your tiles to build a model of each of the numbers in the table below. Then make a sketch of your model in the box. If the number is even, write 1 addition and 1 subtraction equation to match. If the number is odd, write 2 addition and 2 subtraction equations to match.

Number		Sketch	Equations	
ex	9		$4 + 5 = 9$ $9 - 4 = 5$	$5 + 4 = 9$ $9 - 5 = 4$
a	8			
b	5			
c	7			
d	10			

(continued on next page)

Odd & Even Number Review page 2 of 2

4 This is the outline of a number of tiles. Is the number odd or even? Explain your answer.

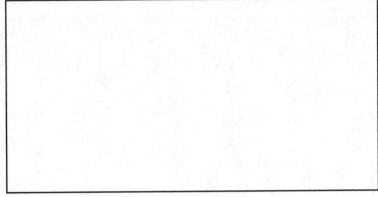

5 **CHALLENGE** Is 31 odd or even? Use numbers, pictures, and words to explain your answer.

NAME

DATE

Addition Table

+	0	1	2	3	4	5	6	7	8	9	10
0	0+0=0	0+1=1	0+2=2	0+3=3	0+4=4	0+5=5	0+6=6	0+7=7	0+8=8	0+9=9	0+10=10
1	1+0=1	1+1=2	1+2=3	1+3=4	1+4=5	1+5=6	1+6=7	1+7=8	1+8=9	1+9=10	1+10=11
2	2+0=2	2+1=3	2+2=4	2+3=5	2+4=6	2+5=7	2+6=8	2+7=9	2+8=10	2+9=11	2+10=12
3	3+0=3	3+1=4	3+2=5	3+3=6	3+4=7	3+5=8	3+6=9	3+7=10	3+8=11	3+9=12	3+10=13
4	4+0=4	4+1=5	4+2=6	4+3=7	4+4=8	4+5=9	4+6=10	4+7=11	4+8=12	4+9=13	4+10=14
5	5+0=5	5+1=6	5+2=7	5+3=8	5+4=9	5+5=10	5+6=11	5+7=12	5+8=13	5+9=14	5+10=15
6	6+0=6	6+1=7	6+2=8	6+3=9	6+4=10	6+5=11	6+6=12	6+7=13	6+8=14	6+9=15	6+10=16
7	7+0=7	7+1=8	7+2=9	7+3=10	7+4=11	7+5=12	7+6=13	7+7=14	7+8=15	7+9=16	7+10=17
8	8+0=8	8+1=9	8+2=10	8+3=11	8+4=12	8+5=13	8+6=14	8+7=15	8+8=16	8+9=17	8+10=18
9	9+0=9	9+1=10	9+2=11	9+3=12	9+4=13	9+5=14	9+6=15	9+7=16	9+8=17	9+9=18	9+10=19
10	10+0=10	10+1=11	10+2=12	10+3=13	10+4=14	10+5=15	10+6=16	10+7=17	10+8=18	10+9=19	10+10=20

Legend

☐	Add Zero facts
☐	Count On facts
☐	Doubles Facts
☐	Doubles Plus or Minus One facts
☐	Make Ten facts
☐	Add Ten facts
☐	Add Nine facts
☐	Leftover facts

NAME | **DATE**

⊞ Scout Out Zeros & Ones

1   Circle all the Add Zero facts in blue. Then take a pencil and go back and do them.

2   Circle all the Count On facts in red. Then take a pencil and go back and do them.

7 + 1 8	6 + 1 7	9 + 0 9	10 + 1 11	0 + 4 4	1 + 8 9	5 + 1 6
1 + 3 4	12 + 1 13	0 + 13 13	17 + 0 17	0 + 4 4	11 + 1 12	1 + 1 2
2 + 1 3	14 + 0 14	1 + 15 16	13 + 1 14	1 + 4 5	13 + 1 14	1 + 9 10

3   Circle all the Zero facts in blue. Then take a pencil and go back and do them.

4   Circle all the Count Back facts in red. Then take a pencil and go back and do them.

7 − 1 6	5 − 1 4	9 − 0 9	10 − 1 9	12 − 0 12	6 − 1 5	7 − 1 6
9 − 1 8	4 − 0 4	18 − 0 18	17 − 1 16	14 − 1 13	8 − 1 7	12 − 1 11
3 − 1 2	15 − 1 14	1 − 1 0	13 − 0 13	6 − 0 6	11 − 1 10	8 − 1 7

NAME | DATE

The Count Back Game

Game 1

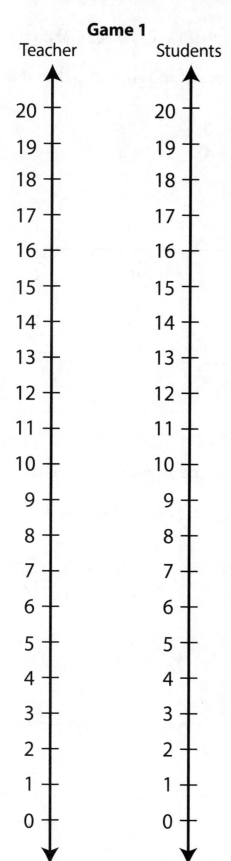

Teacher   Students

Game 2

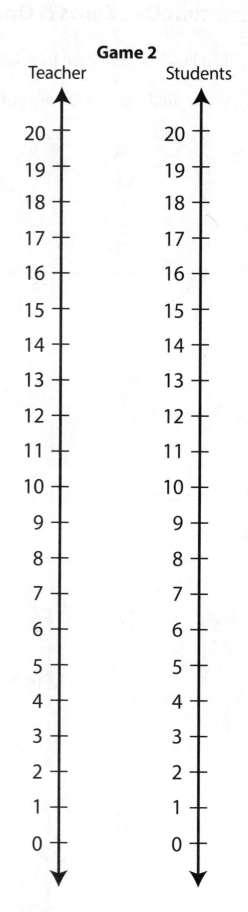

Teacher   Students

The First Century Day page 1 of 2

1 Help Cangaroo hop from 0 to 90.

- First, fill in the missing numbers along the number line.
- Then trace Cangaroo's hops all the way to 90.

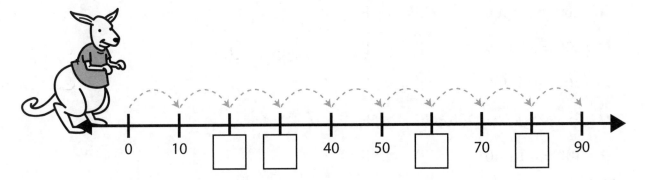

0   10   ☐   ☐   40   50   ☐   70   ☐   90

2 Trace each of the numbers and words below. Then draw a line from each word to the matching expression. (The first one is done for you.)

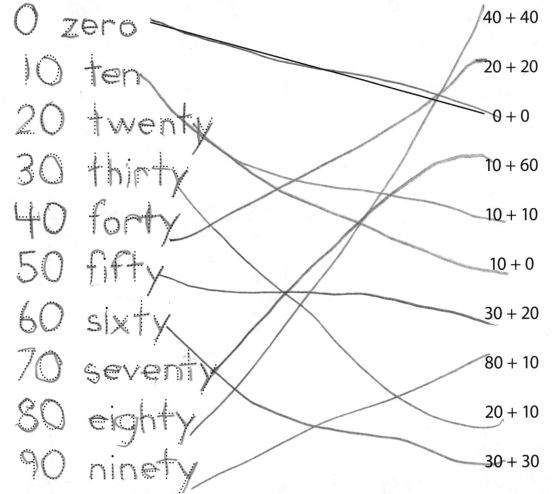

0 zero
10 ten
20 twenty
30 thirty
40 forty
50 fifty
60 sixty
70 seventy
80 eighty
90 ninety

40 + 40
20 + 20
0 + 0
10 + 60
10 + 10
10 + 0
30 + 20
80 + 10
20 + 10
30 + 30

(continued on next page)

NAME _____ | **DATE** _____

The First Century Day page 2 of 2

3   What number comes after 90 when you count by 10s? _____

4   Here are some equations about 100. Some of them are true. Some of them are not.
Circle T (for true) if the equation is correct.
Circle F (for false) if the equation is not correct.

a $40 + 60 = 100$ T   F

b $100 = 50 + 50$ T   F

c $30 + 40 = 100$ T   F

d $25 + 25 + 50 = 100$ T   F

e $100 = 40 + 40$ T   F

f $100 = 100 + 0$ T   F

5   Write four different equations that have 100 as the answer. You can use addition or subtraction equations.

The Second Century Day page 1 of 2

1 Help Cangaroo hop from 100 to 190.

- First, fill in the missing numbers along the number line.
- Then trace Cangaroo's hops all the way to 190.

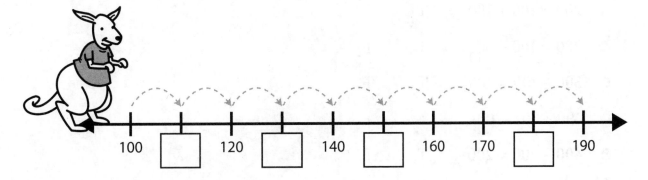

100 ☐ 120 ☐ 140 ☐ 160 170 ☐ 190

2 Trace each of the numbers below. Then draw a line from each number to the matching expression. (The first one is done for you.)

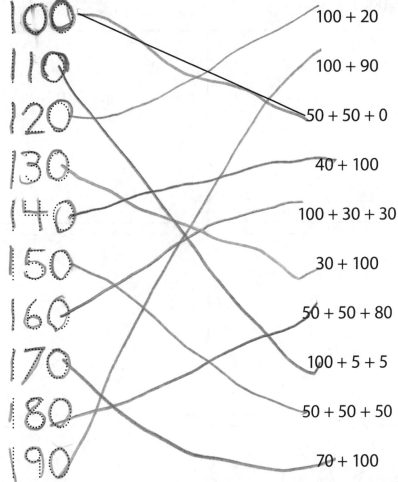

100   100 + 20

110   100 + 90

120   50 + 50 + 0

130   40 + 100

140   100 + 30 + 30

150   30 + 100

160   50 + 50 + 80

170   100 + 5 + 5

180   50 + 50 + 50

190   70 + 100

(continued on next page)

NAME _____ | **DATE** _____

The Second Century Day page 2 of 2

3 What number comes after 190 when you count by 10s? _____

4 Here are some equations about 200. Some of them are true. Some of them are not.
Circle T (for true) if the equation is correct.
Circle F (for false) if the equation is not correct.

   a $200 = 100 + 100$ T   F

   b $200 = 100 + 50$ T   F

   c $300 - 100 = 200$ T   F

   d $190 + 10 = 200$ T   F

   e $400 - 200 = 200$ T   F

   f $200 = 200 + 0$ T   F

5 Write four different equations that have 200 as the answer. You can use addition or subtraction equations.

NAME _____ | DATE _____

Calendar Marker Patterns

1 Here are the calendar markers for the first 21 days of October. Use them to help answer the questions and solve the problems below.

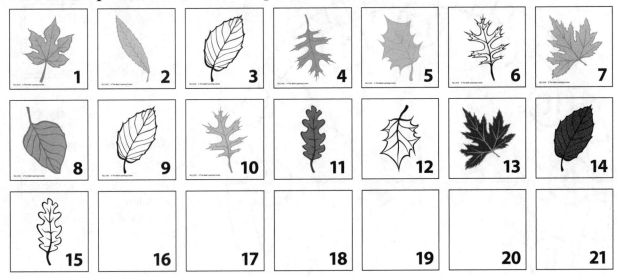

a Circle the markers above that have black and white leaves on them.

b Which of the blank markers in the bottom row should have black and white leaves on them? Color those markers red.

c Write the numbers of the markers that have black and white leaves on them on the lines below. Include the numbers for the markers you colored red.

_____, _____, _____, _____, _____, _____, _____,

d Max says that Marker 24 will have the next black and white leaf. Do you agree with Max? Why or why not?

2 Solve these equations.

$9 +$ _____ $= 12$ $12 + 3 + 3 =$ _____ $3 + 3 + 3 + 3 =$ _____ $15 +$ _____ $= 18$

Five Minutes a Day Record Sheet

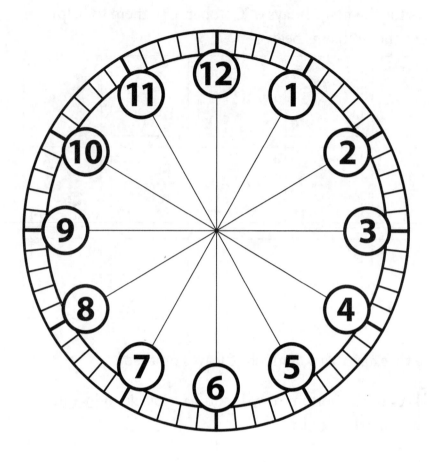

Minutes	Time
Groups of 5 ___ Minutes	
Groups of 5 ___ Minutes	
Groups of 5 ___ Minutes	
Groups of 5 ___ Minutes	
Groups of 5 ___ Minutes	
Groups of 5 ___ Minutes	
Groups of 5 ___ Minutes	
Groups of 5 ___ Minutes	
Groups of 5 ___ Minutes	
Groups of 5 ___ Minutes	
Groups of 5 ___ Minutes	
Groups of 5 ___ Minutes	

How much time have we collected in the first 12 days in class this month?

_____ minutes or _____ hour(s)

NAME _____ | DATE _____

Rolling for Minutes Record Sheet

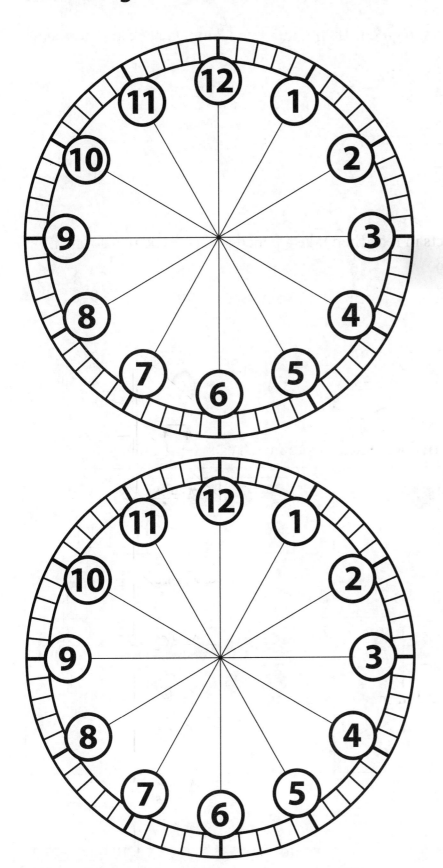

Minutes	Time
Groups of 5 _____ Minutes	
Groups of 5 _____ Minutes	
Groups of 5 _____ Minutes	
Groups of 5 _____ Minutes	
Groups of 5 _____ Minutes	
Groups of 5 _____ Minutes	
Groups of 5 _____ Minutes	
Groups of 5 _____ Minutes	

How much time did we collect in all this month, counting the first 12 days?

_____ minutes

NAME _____ | DATE _____

Scout Out Tens

1 Circle all the Make Ten facts in green. Then take a pencil and go back and do them.

6	5	3	2	9	4	9
+ 4	+ 5	+ 1	+ 8	+ 0	+ 6	+ 1

3	5	7	8	10	1	0
+ 7	+ 3	+ 3	+ 2	+ 0	+ 9	+ 10

2 Circle all the Break Ten facts in red. Then take a pencil and go back and do them.

10	10	9	10	10	8	10
− 5	− 2	− 5	− 8	− 3	− 6	− 0

10	10	12	10	10	10	10
− 6	− 1	− 12	− 7	− 10	− 9	− 4

3 Write 2 addition and 2 subtraction equations to match each ten-frame.

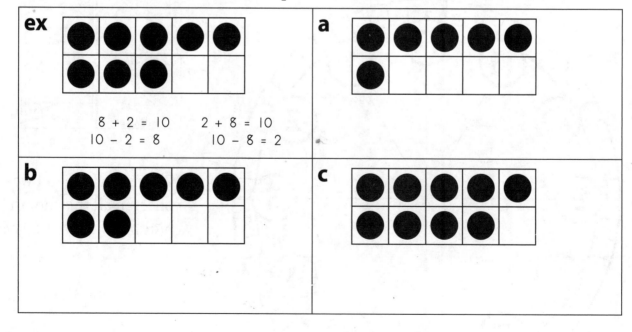

ex

8 + 2 = 10   2 + 8 = 10
10 − 2 = 8   10 − 8 = 2

a

b

c

4 Fill in the missing numbers.

$4 + \underline{\quad} = 10$ $10 = 5 + \underline{\quad}$ $10 - \underline{\quad} = 7$ $10 - \underline{\quad} = 2$

NAME _____ **| DATE** _____

 The Third Century Day page 1 of 2

1 Help Cangaroo hop from 200 to 290.

- First, fill in the missing numbers along the number line.
- Then trace Cangaroo's hops all the way to 290.

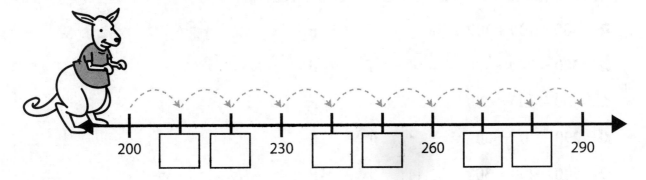

200 | ☐ | ☐ | 230 | ☐ | ☐ | 260 | ☐ | ☐ | 290

2 Trace each of the numbers below. Then draw a line from each word to the matching expression. (The first one is done for you.)

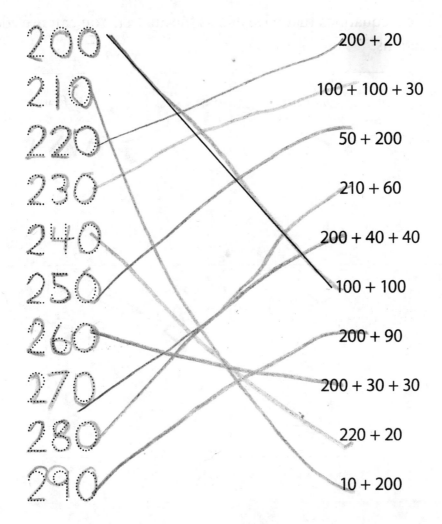

200		200 + 20
210		100 + 100 + 30
220		50 + 200
230		210 + 60
240		200 + 40 + 40
250		100 + 100
260		200 + 90
270		200 + 30 + 30
280		220 + 20
290		10 + 200

The Third Century Day page 2 of 2

3 What number comes after 290 when you count by 10s? _____

4 Here are some equations about 300. Some of them are true. Some of them are not.
Circle T (for true) if the equation is correct.
Circle F (for false) if the equation is not correct.

a $300 = 100 + 100 + 100$ T   F

b $300 = 200 + 100$ T   F

c $400 - 200 = 300$ T   F

d $290 + 10 = 300$ T   F

e $500 - 200 = 300$ T   F

f $300 = 0 + 300$ T   F

5 Write four different equations that have 300 as the answer. You can use addition or subtraction equations.

The Fourth Century Day page 1 of 2

1 Help Cangaroo hop from 300 to 390.

- First, fill in the missing numbers along the number line.
- Then trace Cangaroo's hops all the way to 390.

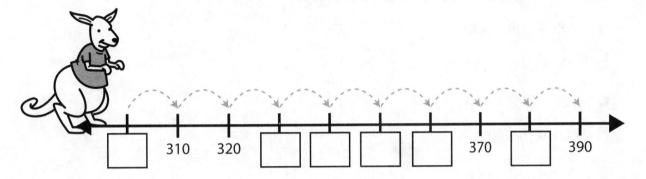

| | 310 | 320 | | | | | 370 | | 390 |

2 Trace each of the numbers below. Then draw a line from each word to the matching expression. (The first one is done for you.)

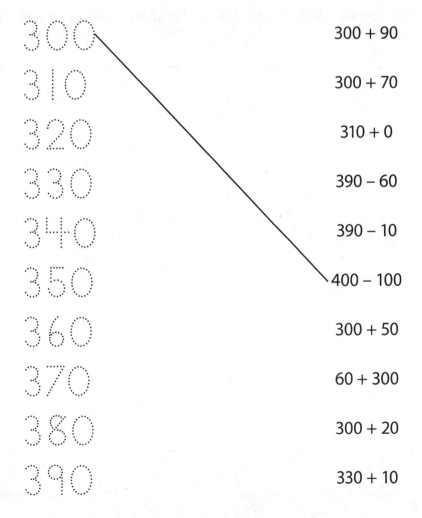

300   300 + 90

310   300 + 70

320   310 + 0

330   390 − 60

340   390 − 10

350   400 − 100

360   300 + 50

370   60 + 300

380   300 + 20

390   330 + 10

The Fourth Century Day page 2 of 2

3 What number comes after 300 when you count by 10s? _____

4 Here are some equations about 400. Some of them are true. Some of them are not.
Circle T (for true) if the equation is correct.
Circle F (for false) if the equation is not correct.

  a $200 + 200 = 400$ T   F

  b $400 = 300 + 100$ T   F

  c $600 - 300 = 400$ T   F

  d $390 + 10 = 400$ T   F

  e $300 - 200 = 400$ T   F

  f $400 = 100 + 100 + 100 + 100$ T   F

5 Write four different equations that have 400 as the answer. You can use addition or subtraction equations.

Telling Time on Two Kinds of Clocks page 1 of 2

1 Read each of these clock faces and write the time on the digital clock.

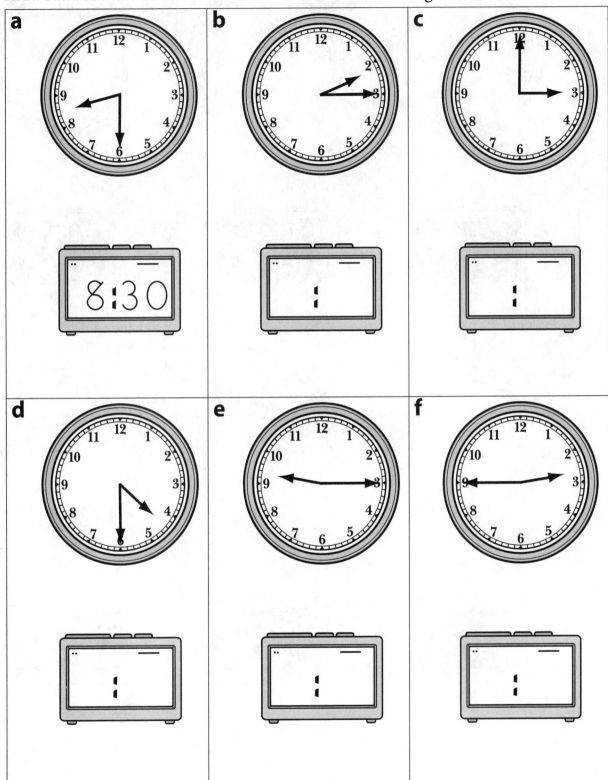

(continued on next page)

Telling Time on Two Kinds of Clocks page 2 of 2

2 Draw hour and minute hands on the clock faces to show the times below.

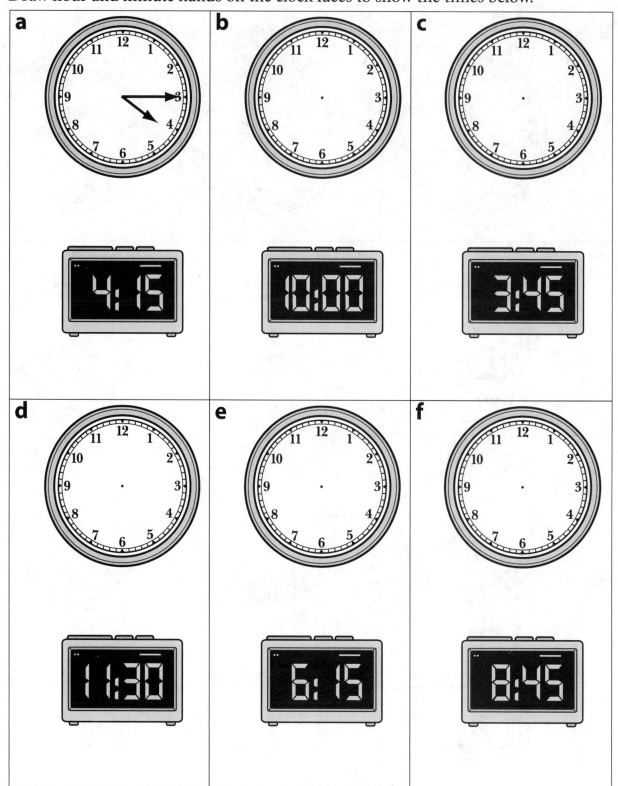

NAME _____ | **DATE** _____

 Measure It Twice Record Sheet page 1 of 2

1 Estimate and measure the length, width, or height of each of the objects son this page and the next when the card comes up during Calendar Collector activities this month.

Object to Measure	Estimate (sticks)	Actual Length (sticks)	Estimate (cubes)	Actual Length (cubes)
A Bookshelf				
A Teacher				
A Calendar Grid				
A Door				
A Chair				

(continued on next page)

25

Measure It Twice Record Sheet page 2 of 2

Object to Measure	Estimate (sticks)	Actual Length (sticks)	Estimate (cubes)	Actual Length (cubes)
A Table				
A Work Place Bin				
A Kid				
A Book				

2 The second graders used craft sticks to measure their teacher's desk. The desk was 15 sticks long. Then they estimated how long the desk was in cubes. Here are four of their estimates.

a Which estimate makes the best sense?

○ 15 cubes   ○ 7 cubes   ○ 85 cubes   ○ 30 cubes

b Why?

3 Anna and Sam measured the length of the same table. Anna says the table is 10 units long. Sam says the table is 60 units long.

a Who was using the longer unit?

b How do you know?

⊞ **Doubles Up** page 1 of 2

Doubles	**Doubles Plus or Minus One**	**Discards**

(continued on next page)

27

NAME _____ | **DATE** _____

Doubles Up page 2 of 2

Doubles	**Doubles Plus or Minus One**	**Discards**

28

NAME _____ | **DATE** _____

⊞ Scout Out Doubles & Halves

1 Circle all the Doubles in blue. Then take a pencil and go back and do them.
Circle all the Doubles Plus or Minus One in red. Then take a pencil and go back and
do them.

7	6	9	10	3	8	5
+ 7	+ 6	+ 10	+ 9	+ 4	+ 8	+ 5

3	4	6	10	2	3	7
+ 3	+ 4	+ 7	+ 10	+ 2	+ 2	+ 8

7	6	9	8	8	5	4
+ 6	+ 5	+ 9	+ 7	+ 9	+ 6	+ 5

2 Circle all the Take All facts in blue. Then take a pencil and go back and do them.
Circle all the Take Half facts in red. Then take a pencil and go back and do them.

7	10	10	14	12	15	8
− 7	− 5	− 10	− 14	− 6	− 15	− 4

14	11	6	16	13	20	18
− 7	− 11	− 3	− 8	− 13	− 10	− 9

3 Fill in the missing numbers.

8 + ___ = 16   6 + ____ = 12   ___ + 9 = 18   ____ + 10 = 20

16 − ___ = 0   14 − ___ = 7   10 − ____ = 5   12 − ____ = 0

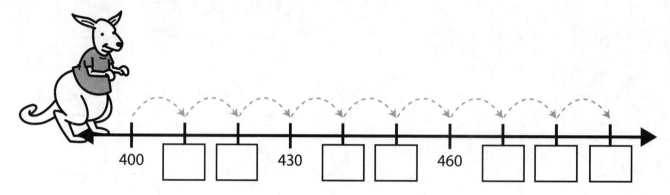

The Fifth Century Day page 1 of 2

1 Help Cangaroo hop from 400 to 490.

- First, fill in the missing numbers along the number line.
- Then trace Cangaroo's hops all the way to 490.

400 ☐ ☐ 430 ☐ ☐ 460 ☐ ☐ ☐

2 Trace each of the numbers below. Then draw a line from each number to the description that matches best. (The first one is done for you.)

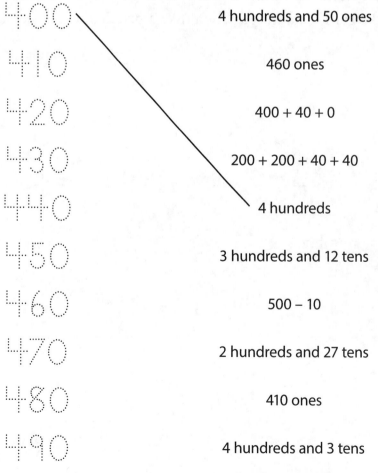

400	4 hundreds and 50 ones
410	460 ones
420	400 + 40 + 0
430	200 + 200 + 40 + 40
440	4 hundreds
450	3 hundreds and 12 tens
460	500 – 10
470	2 hundreds and 27 tens
480	410 ones
490	4 hundreds and 3 tens

(continued on next page)

The Fifth Century Day page 2 of 2

3 What number comes after 400 when you count by hundreds? _____

4 Count the collection of sticks in each box and record an equation to show how many there are in all. (There are 100 sticks in each big bundle, and 10 sticks in each small bundle.)

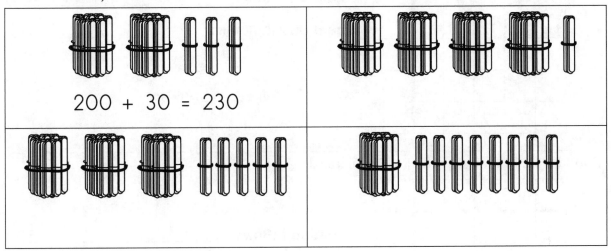

$$200 + 30 = 230$$

5 Write 4 different equations that have 500 as the answer. You can use addition or subtraction equations.

NAME _____ | **DATE** _____

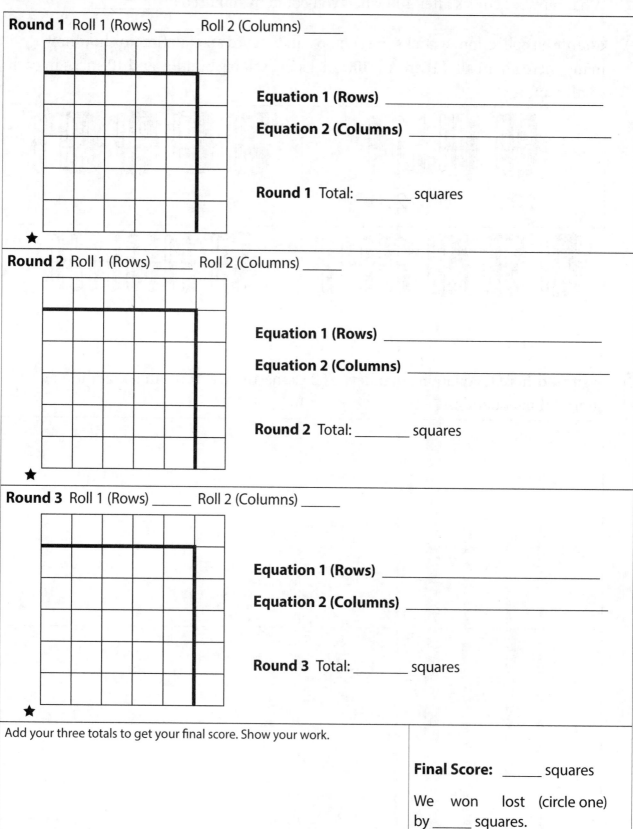

Rows & Columns Record Sheet

Round 1 Roll 1 (Rows) _____ Roll 2 (Columns) _____

Equation 1 (Rows) _____

Equation 2 (Columns) _____

Round 1 Total: _____ squares

Round 2 Roll 1 (Rows) _____ Roll 2 (Columns) _____

Equation 1 (Rows) _____

Equation 2 (Columns) _____

Round 2 Total: _____ squares

Round 3 Roll 1 (Rows) _____ Roll 2 (Columns) _____

Equation 1 (Rows) _____

Equation 2 (Columns) _____

Round 3 Total: _____ squares

Add your three totals to get your final score. Show your work.

Final Score: _____ squares

We won lost (circle one) by _____ squares.

32

NAME _____ | **DATE** _____

Rows & Columns Record Sheet

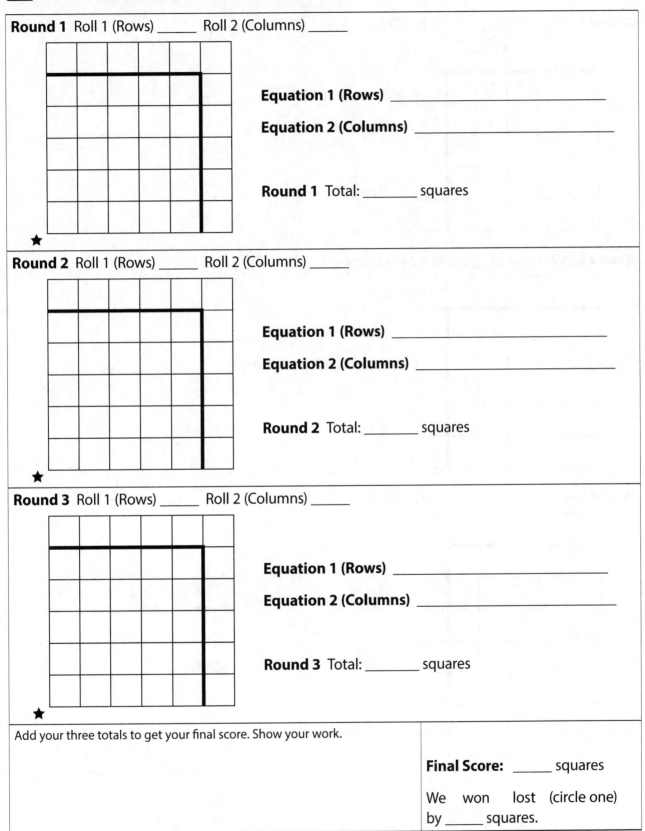

Round 1 Roll 1 (Rows) _____ Roll 2 (Columns) _____

Equation 1 (Rows) _____

Equation 2 (Columns) _____

Round 1 Total: _____ squares

Round 2 Roll 1 (Rows) _____ Roll 2 (Columns) _____

Equation 1 (Rows) _____

Equation 2 (Columns) _____

Round 2 Total: _____ squares

Round 3 Roll 1 (Rows) _____ Roll 2 (Columns) _____

Equation 1 (Rows) _____

Equation 2 (Columns) _____

Round 3 Total: _____ squares

Add your three totals to get your final score. Show your work.

Final Score: _____ squares

We won lost (circle one) by _____ squares.

NAME _____ | DATE _____

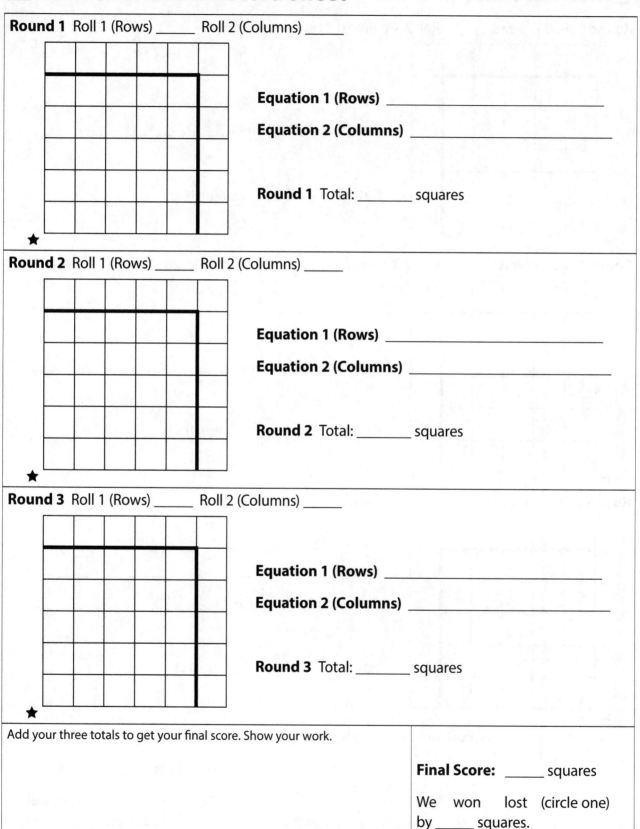

Rows & Columns Record Sheet

Round 1 Roll 1 (Rows) _____ Roll 2 (Columns) _____

Equation 1 (Rows) _____

Equation 2 (Columns) _____

Round 1 Total: _____ squares

Round 2 Roll 1 (Rows) _____ Roll 2 (Columns) _____

Equation 1 (Rows) _____

Equation 2 (Columns) _____

Round 2 Total: _____ squares

Round 3 Roll 1 (Rows) _____ Roll 2 (Columns) _____

Equation 1 (Rows) _____

Equation 2 (Columns) _____

Round 3 Total: _____ squares

Add your three totals to get your final score. Show your work.

Final Score: _____ squares

We won lost (circle one) by _____ squares.

⊞ The Tens & Nines Game

Add Tens	**Add Nines**	**Discards**

35

NAME _____ | DATE _____

⊞ Tens & Nines

1 Complete the Add Ten facts.

10	3	4	10	10	9	10
+ 2	+ 10	+ 10	+ 5	+ 7	+ 10	+ 8

2 Complete the Add Nine facts.

9	3	5	9	9	6	9
+ 2	+ 9	+ 9	+ 7	+ 4	+ 9	+ 8

3 Complete the Take Away Ten subtraction facts.

18	12	15	17	13	16	14
− 10	− 10	− 10	− 10	− 10	− 10	− 10

4 Complete the Back to Ten subtraction facts.

17	13	15	14	16	18	12
− 7	− 3	− 5	− 4	− 6	− 8	− 2

5 Make up an equation for each strategy and show what it means by drawing dots in the squares on the ten-strips. (The first one has been done for you.)

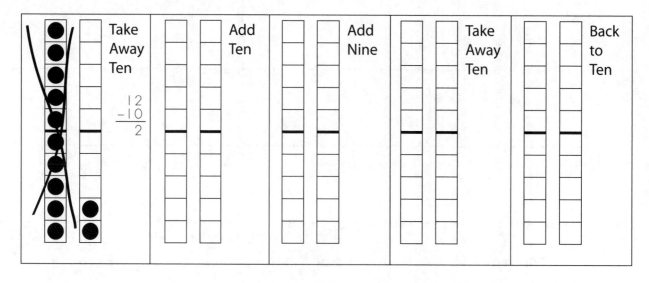

The Sixth Century Day page 1 of 2

1 Help Cangaroo hop from 500 to 590.

- First, fill in the missing numbers along the number line.
- Then trace Cangaroo's hops to 530 and draw the rest yourself as you count by 10s.

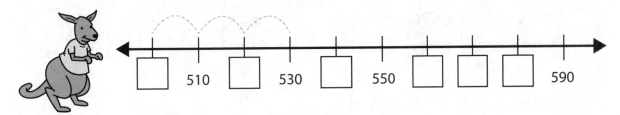

510   530   550   590

2 Trace each of the numbers below. Then draw a line from each number to the description that matches best. (The first one is done for you.)

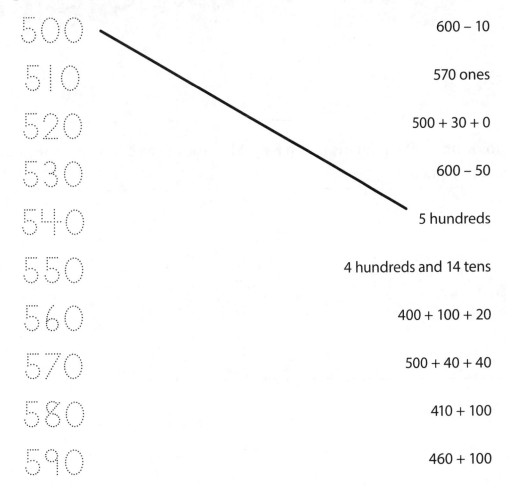

500

510

520

530

540

550

560

570

580

590

600 – 10

570 ones

500 + 30 + 0

600 – 50

5 hundreds

4 hundreds and 14 tens

400 + 100 + 20

500 + 40 + 40

410 + 100

460 + 100

NAME _____ | **DATE** _____

The Sixth Century Day page 2 of 2

3 What number comes after 500 when you count by hundreds? _____

4 Count the collection of sticks in each box and record an equation to show how many there are in all. (There are 100 sticks in each big bundle, and 10 sticks in each small bundle.)

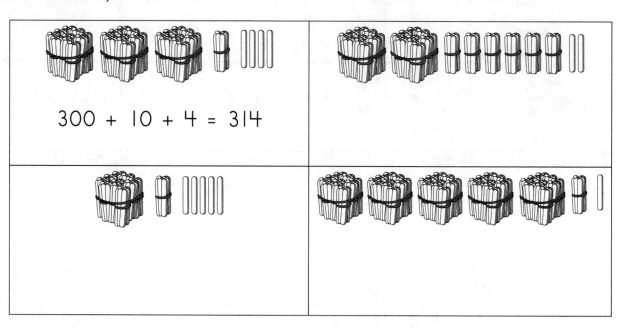

300 + 10 + 4 = 314

5 Write four different equations that have 600 as the answer. You can use addition or subtraction equations.

⊞ The Seventh Century Day page 1 of 2

1 Help Cangaroo hop from 600 to 690.

- First, fill in the missing numbers along the number line.
- Then trace Cangaroo's hop to 610 and draw the rest yourself as you count by 10s.

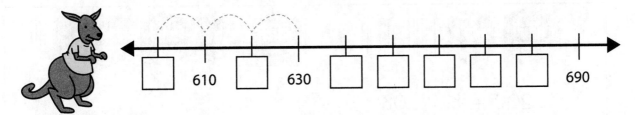

610   630   690

2 Trace each of the numbers below. Then draw a line from each number to the description that matches best. (The first one is done for you.)

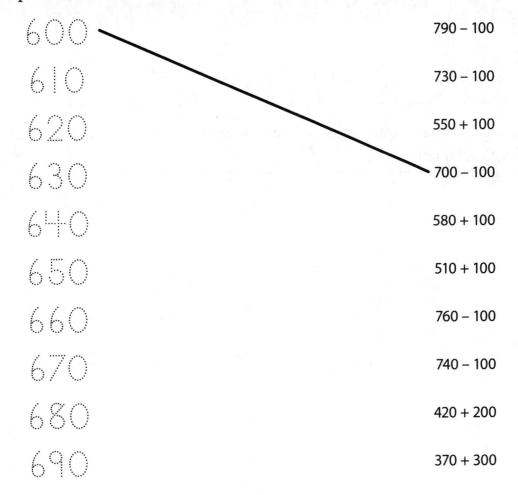

600   790 – 100

610   730 – 100

620   550 + 100

630   700 – 100

640   580 + 100

650   510 + 100

660   760 – 100

670   740 – 100

680   420 + 200

690   370 + 300

NAME _____ | **DATE** _____

The Seventh Century Day page 2 of 2

3 What number comes after 600 when you count by hundreds? _____

4 Count the collection of sticks in each box and record an equation to show how many there are in all. (There are 100 sticks in each big bundle, and 10 sticks in each small bundle.)

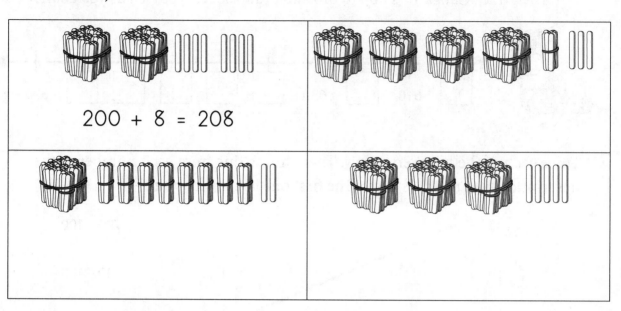

200 + 8 = 208

5 Write four different equations that have 700 as the answer. You can use addition or subtraction equations.

NAME _____ | DATE _____

The Sixth Graph

Here is a picture of the sixth graph on the calendar markers this month.

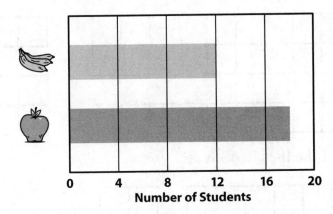

Number of Students

1 Someone made this graph after asking some second graders a survey question. What question did they probably ask?

2 What kind of graph is this? Fill in the bubble to show.

○ picture graph   ○ bar graph

3 Use numbers and equations to answer the questions below.

a How many students does each section of the graph show?_____

b How many students chose bananas? _____

c How many students chose apples?_____

d How many students took part in this survey? Write an equation to show.

e How many more students chose apples than bananas? Write an equation to show.

4 Write a good title for this graph. _____

NAME _____ **DATE** _____

 # Tile Fractions

Color in *exactly half* of the tiles in each set.

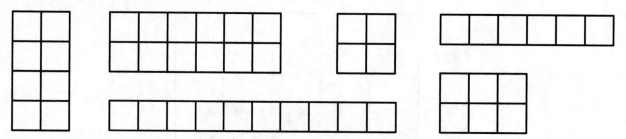

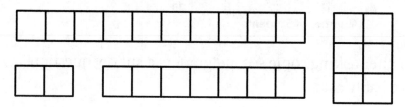

Color in *more than half* of the tiles in each set.

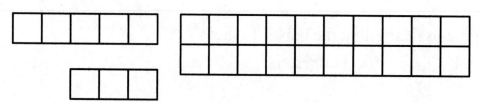

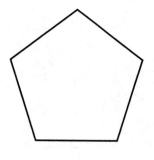

Color in *fewer than half* of the tiles in each set.

Draw a line to divide each shape in half.

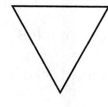

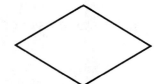

Draw, Add & Compare Record Sheet page 1 of 2

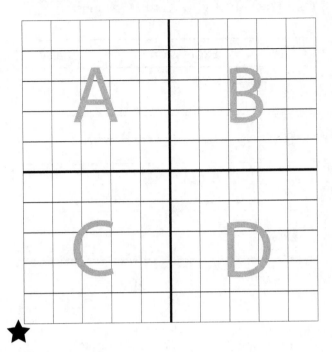

Card 1 (Rows) _____ Card 2 (Columns) _____

Quad	Expression	Squares	
A			
B			
C			
D			
	TOTAL		

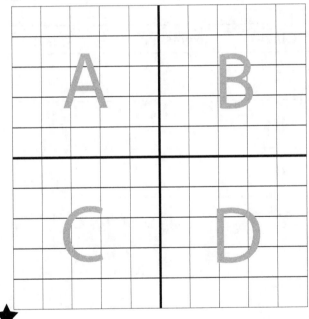

Card 1 (Rows) _____ Card 2 (Columns) _____

Quad	Expression	Squares	
A			
B			
C			
D			
	TOTAL		

My team (circle one)

won   lost

+ ☐☐

Final Score ☐☐☐ by _____ squares

Draw, Add & Compare Record Sheet page 2 of 2

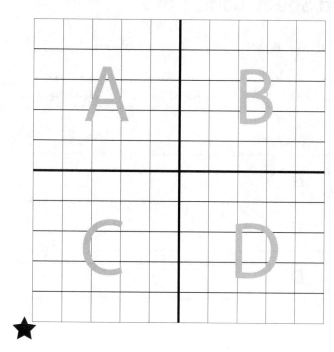

Card 1 (Rows) _____ Card 2 (Columns) _____

Quad	Expression	Squares	
A			
B			
C			
D			
		TOTAL	

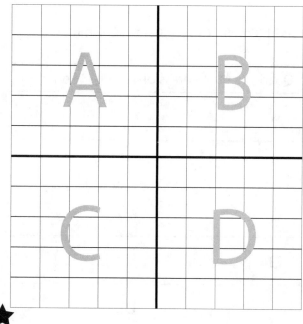

Card 1 (Rows) _____ Card 2 (Columns) _____

Quad	Expression	Squares	
A			
B			
C			
D			
		TOTAL	

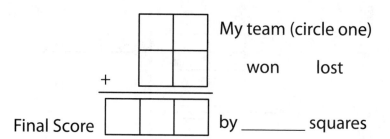

My team (circle one)

won   lost

Final Score [ ][ ][ ] by _____ squares

NAME

DATE

Fact Strategy Game Record Sheet

	Doubles	Doubles Plus or Minus One	Make Tens	Add Tens	Add Nines	Leftovers
Round 1						
Round 2						
Round 3						

⊞ Up to Ten Game Record Sheet

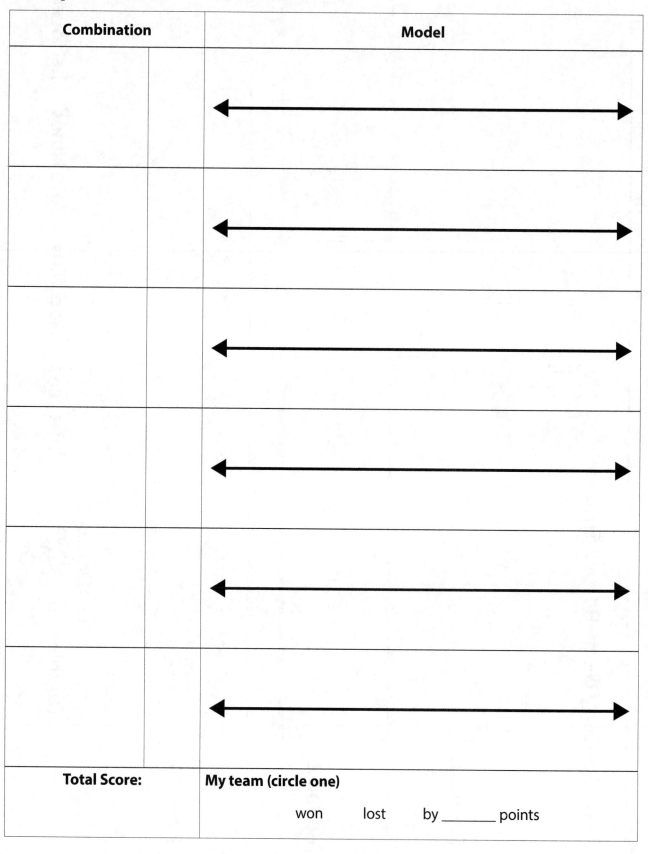

Combination		Model
Total Score:		**My team (circle one)** won lost by _____ points

46

⊞ Up to Ten

One way to solve subtraction problems is to think about what you need to add to the smaller number to get to the larger number. For example, if you are trying to solve 14 – 8, you can think, "OK, if I start at 8, I need 2 more to get up to 10, and then it's 4 more. So 14 – 8 must be 6."

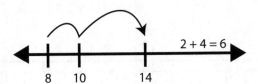

$8 + 6 = 14$, so $14 - 8 = 6$

1 Use the open number line to model the Up to Ten strategy, and use your model to help find the answer.

ex 15 – 7

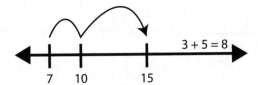

$7 + \underline{\ 8\ } = 15$, so $15 - 7 = \underline{\ 8\ }$

a 16 – 9

$9 + \underline{\ \ \ \ } = 16$, so $16 - 9 = \underline{\ \ \ \ }$

b 13 – 5

$5 + \underline{\ \ \ \ } = 13$, so $13 - 5 = \underline{\ \ \ \ }$

c 12 – 7

$7 + \underline{\ \ \ \ } = 12$, so $12 - 7 = \underline{\ \ \ \ }$

2 Use the Up to Ten strategy to solve each of the problems below.

13	15	11	16	14	12	11
– 8	– 9	– 5	– 7	– 6	– 5	– 8

NAME | **DATE**

Changing Endpoints

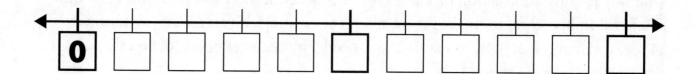

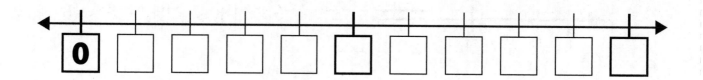

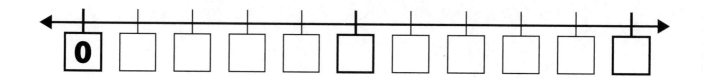

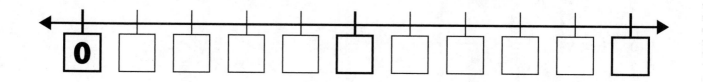

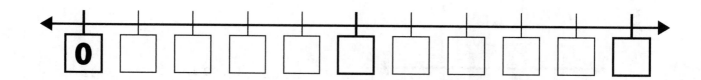

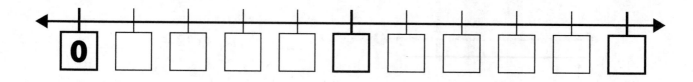

The Eighth Century Day page 1 of 2

1 Help Cangaroo hop from 700 to 790.

  - First, fill in the missing numbers along the number line.

  - Then trace Cangaroo's hop to 710 and draw the rest yourself as you count by 10s.

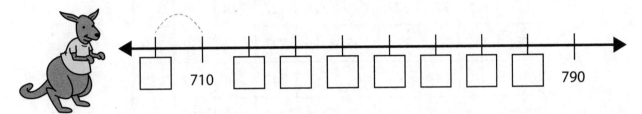

710   790

2 Trace each of the numbers below. Then write an expression to describe each number. The first one is done for you. Trace that one and write your own for the rest of the numbers.

700	400 + 200 + 50 + 50
710	400 + 300 + 10 = 710
720	100 + 600 + 10 + 10
730	
740	
750	
760	
770	
780	
790	

NAME _____ | DATE _____

The Eighth Century Day page 2 of 2

3 Fill in the missing numbers on this grid.

701	702		704	705	706		708	709	710
711	712	713		715	716	717	718		720
	722	723	724		726	727	728	729	
731	732		734	735	736	737		739	740
741		743	744	745		747	748	749	750
751	752	753	754		756	757	758	759	
	762	763	764	765	766		768	769	770
771	772	773		775	776	777	778		780
781		783	784	785		787	788	789	790
791	792	793	794		796	797		799	800

4 Make a picture by coloring in some of the squares on the grid above.

a Solve each combination below. Then color the answers on the grid red.

700 + 30 + 4	745 – 1	700 + 37	400 + 300 + 47
760 – 4	100 + 600 + 57	789 – 2	780 + 5
700 + 80 + 4	700 + 80 + 6	780 – 2	500 + 200 + 35
700 + 30 + 6	780 – 3	745 + 10	646 + 100
643 + 100	743 + 10	755 – 10	744 + 10
738 + 10	778 – 10	757 + 10	876 – 100
748 + 10	700 + 60 + 6	773 – 10	300 + 400 + 65
675 + 100	764 + 10	700 + 70 + 3	700 + 60 + 4

b Solve each combination below. Color the first two answers on the grid brown. Then color the last two answers on the grid green.

736 – 10   700 + 16 | 700 + 20 + 7   708 + 10

The Ninth Century Day page 1 of 2

1 Help Cangaroo hop from 800 to 890.

- First, fill in the missing numbers along the number line.
- Then trace Cangaroo's hop to 810 and draw the rest yourself as you count by 10s.

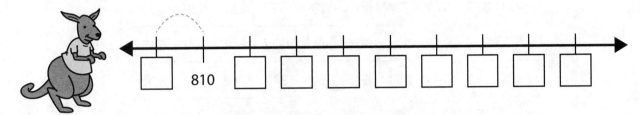

810

2 Trace each of the numbers below. Then write an expression to describe each number. The first one is done for you. Trace that one and write your own for the rest of the numbers.

800	950 – 150
810	
820	
830	
840	
850	
860	
870	
880	
890	

The Ninth Century Day page 2 of 2

3 Fill in the missing numbers on this grid.

801	802	803	804	805	806	807	808	809	810
811	812	813	814	815	816	817	818	819	820
821	822	823	824	825	826	827	828	829	830
831	832	833	834	835	836	837	838	839	840
841	842	843	844	845	846	847	848	849	850
851	852	853	854	855	856	857	858	859	860
861	862	863	864	865	866	867	868	869	870
871	872	873	874	875	876	877	878	879	880
881	882	883	884	885	886	887	888	889	890
891	892	893	894	895	896	897	898	899	900

4 Make a picture by coloring in some of the squares on the grid above.

a Solve each combination below. Then color the answers on the grid yellow.

715 + 100 815   916 – 100 816   800 + 50 + 2 852   860 – 1 859

825 – 1 824   800 + 30 + 4 834   834 + 10 844   700 + 127 827

827 + 10 837   857 – 10 847   800 + 25 825   825 + 1 826

825 + 10 835   800 + 36 836   852 + 10 862   879 – 10 869

872 + 0 872   800 + 70 + 9 879   782 + 100 882   899 – 10 889

745 + 100 845   946 – 100 846

b Solve each combination below. Then color the answers on the grid blue.

800 + 50 + 3 853   765 + 100 865   848 + 10 858   800 + 66 866

963 – 100 863   878 – 10 868   754 + 100 854   800 + 50 + 7 857

764 + 100 864   870 – 3 867   800 + 25 + 25 + 5 855   956 – 100 856

🎨 **Capture the Clock** page 1 of 4

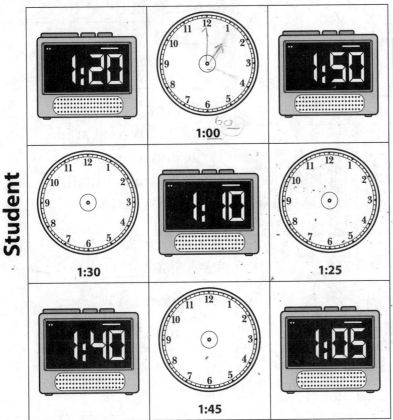

Student

1:20	1:00	1:50
1:30	1:10	1:25
1:40	1:45	1:05

Game 1 1:00

Class	Teacher

Clock Problems

I am usually asleep at 1:00
(circle one)

a.m.   **p.m.**

I am usually at school at 1:15
(circle one)

a.m.   **p.m.**

At 1:30 p.m. on a school day, I
am usually

Student

3:35	3:05	3:00
3:45	3:30	3:20
3:15	3:50	3:55

Game 2 3:00

Class	Teacher

Clock Problems

At 3:00 p.m., I am usually

At 3:25 a.m., I am usually

Sara is in second grade. She
goes to soccer practice at 3:45
(circle one)

a.m.   **p.m.**

Capture the Clock page 2 of 4

Student

5:25   5:05   5:35

5:00   5:45   5:15

5:40   5:20   5:55

Game 3 5:00

Class	Teacher

Clock Problems

Jamal is in second grade. Write **a.m.** or **p.m.** to show when he would usually do the things on this list.

Soccer practice 5:00 _____

Sleep 5:30 _____

Homework 5:45 _____

Wake up 5:55 _____

Student

6:20   6:05   6:50

6:45   6:30   6:10

6:25   6:00   6:40

Game 4 6:00

Class	Teacher

Clock Problems

Draw a line from each meal to the time people would usually eat this kind of food.

6:15 a.m.

6:15 p.m.

54

Capture the Clock page 3 of 4

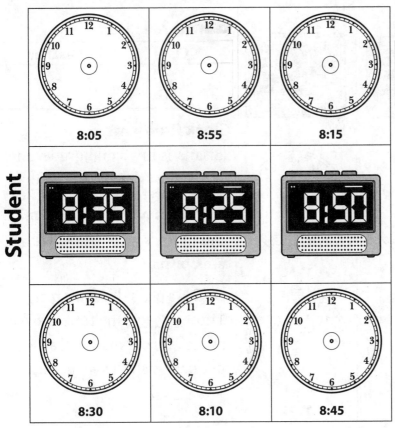

Game 5 8:00

Class	Teacher

Clock Problems

At 8:30 p.m. on a school night, I am usually

At 8:30 p.m. on a weekend night, I am usually

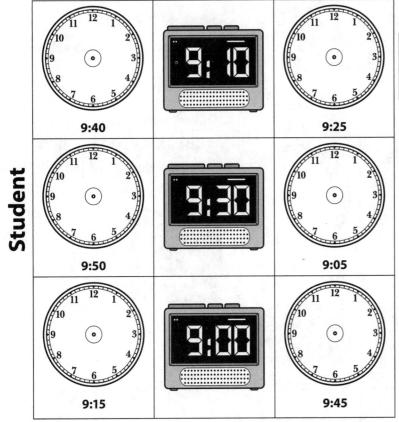

Game 6 9:00

Class	Teacher

Clock Problems

Rosa is in second grade. Write a.m. or p.m. to show when she would usually do the things on the list.

Reading group 9:20 _____

Maker her bed on Saturday morning 9:10 _____

Go to bed on Saturday night 9:30 _____

NAME _____ | **DATE** _____

Capture the Clock page 4 of 4

11:20	11:05	11:45
11:35	11:10	11:50
11:00	11:30	11:15

(Student)

Game 7 11:00

Class	Teacher

Clock Problems

Briana is in second grade. She is usually asleep at (circle one)

11:20 a.m.   **11:20 p.m.**

Fill in the spaces below with a.m. or p.m.

Briana's class does math at 11:00 _____. One time she fell asleep during math because her baby sister woke her up at 11:25 _____.

12:50	12:00	12:20
12:05	12:45	12:30
12:10	12:25	12:40

(Student)

Game 8 12:00

Class	Teacher

Clock Problems

Write a.m. or p.m. to show when people would usually use these things.

12:30

12:10

NAME _____ | **DATE** _____

 Base Ten Bank Addition

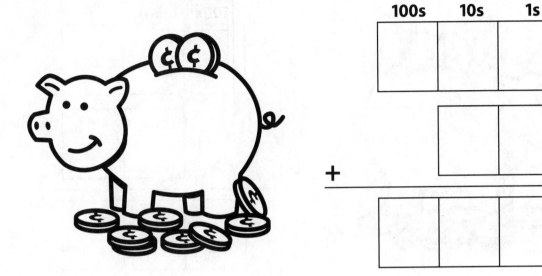

Show your work here.

Base Ten Bank Addition

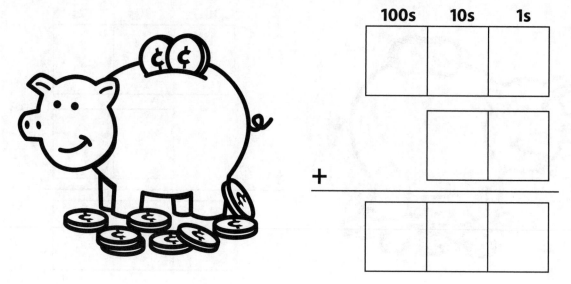

Show your work here.

Base Ten Bank Addition

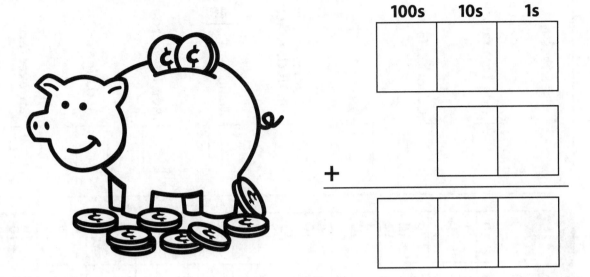

Show your work here.

NAME _____ | **DATE** _____

Addition Table for Fact Mastery

Legend

☐	Add Zero facts
☐	Count On facts
☐	Doubles facts
☐	Doubles Plus or Minus One facts
☐	Make Ten facts
☐	Add Ten facts
☐	Add Nine facts
☐	Leftover facts

+	0	1	2	3	4	5	6	7	8	9	10
0	0+0=0	0+1=1	0+2=2	0+3=3	0+4=4	0+5=5	0+6=6	0+7=7	0+8=8	0+9=9	0+10=10
1	1+0=1	1+1=2	1+2=3	1+3=4	1+4=5	1+5=6	1+6=7	1+7=8	1+8=9	1+9=10	1+10=11
2	2+0=2	2+1=3	2+2=4	2+3=5	2+4=6	2+5=7	2+6=8	2+7=9	2+8=10	2+9=11	2+10=12
3	3+0=3	3+1=4	3+2=5	3+3=6	3+4=7	3+5=8	3+6=9	3+7=10	3+8=11	3+9=12	3+10=13
4	4+0=4	4+1=5	4+2=6	4+3=7	4+4=8	4+5=9	4+6=10	4+7=11	4+8=12	4+9=13	4+10=14
5	5+0=5	5+1=6	5+2=7	5+3=8	5+4=9	5+5=10	5+6=11	5+7=12	5+8=13	5+9=14	5+10=15
6	6+0=6	6+1=7	6+2=8	6+3=9	6+4=10	6+5=11	6+6=12	6+7=13	6+8=14	6+9=15	6+10=16
7	7+0=7	7+1=8	7+2=9	7+3=10	7+4=11	7+5=12	7+6=13	7+7=14	7+8=15	7+9=16	7+10=17
8	8+0=8	8+1=9	8+2=10	8+3=11	8+4=12	8+5=13	8+6=14	8+7=15	8+8=16	8+9=17	8+10=18
9	9+0=9	9+1=10	9+2=11	9+3=12	9+4=13	9+5=14	9+6=15	9+7=16	9+8=17	9+9=18	9+10=19
10	10+0=10	10+1=11	10+2=12	10+3=13	10+4=14	10+5=15	10+6=16	10+7=17	10+8=18	10+9=19	10+10=20

⊞ Scout Them Out Addition A

1 Circle the strategy you are practicing today.

Count On   Make Ten   Doubles   Doubles Plus or Minus One   Add Nine   Add Ten

2 Look at the facts below. Circle the facts you can solve using the strategy you chose.

3 Solve the circled facts first. Then solve the rest of the facts if you have time.

6	7	10	9	7	6	3
+ 7	+ 9	+ 7	+ 2	+ 3	+ 10	+ 9

9	8	8	9	9	5	2
+ 4	+ 3	+ 1	+ 2	+ 9	+ 2	+ 7

4	10	5	3	6	8	6
+ 6	+ 9	+ 5	+ 3	+ 5	+ 7	+ 6

5	1	3	7	3	9	4
+ 3	+ 7	+ 6	+ 7	+ 4	+ 8	+ 5

8	2	5	9	9	3	8
+ 8	+ 8	+ 9	+ 6	+ 8	+ 8	+ 10

4 Use the facts you circled to write four different subtraction problems in the boxes below. Then find the differences.

_____ – _____ =	_____ – _____ =	_____ – _____ =	_____ – _____ =

NAME _____ **| DATE** _____

⊞ Scout Them Out Addition B

1 Circle the strategy you are practicing today.

Count On   Make Ten   Doubles   Doubles Plus or Minus One   Add Nine   Add Ten

2 Look at the facts below. Circle the facts you can solve using the strategy you chose.

3 Solve the circled facts first. Then solve the rest of the facts if you have time.

7	4	6	2	2	9	8
+ 6	+ 3	+ 6	+ 5	+ 9	+ 3	+ 2

7	5	9	2	6	8	7
+ 8	+ 6	+ 7	+ 9	+ 4	+ 9	+ 2

8	4	6	8	8	10	5
+ 8	+ 9	+ 9	+ 9	+ 3	+ 8	+ 5

3	7	10	5	1	3	9
+ 8	+ 7	+ 6	+ 4	+ 8	+ 5	+ 9

7	3	6	7	9	3	9
+ 10	+ 3	+ 3	+ 1	+ 10	+ 7	+ 5

4 Use the facts you circled to write four different subtraction problems in the boxes below. Then find the differences.

_____ – _____ =	_____ – _____ =	_____ – _____ =	_____ – _____ =

62

🔢 Scout Them Out Addition C

1 Circle the strategy you are practicing today.

Count On   Make Ten   Doubles   Doubles Plus or Minus One   Add Nine   Add Ten

2 Look at the facts below. Circle the facts you can solve using the strategy you chose.

3 Solve the circled facts first. Then solve the rest of the facts if you have time.

9 + 3	3 + 8	7 + 7	5 + 6	9 + 7	6 + 6	3 + 5
6 + 3	5 + 4	7 + 1	2 + 5	1 + 8	9 + 5	2 + 9
4 + 3	7 + 6	8 + 9	4 + 9	7 + 2	9 + 9	7 + 10
6 + 4	7 + 8	10 + 6	3 + 7	2 + 9	8 + 8	8 + 2
6 + 9	8 + 9	10 + 8	9 + 10	5 + 5	8 + 3	3 + 3

4 Use the facts you circled to write four different subtraction problems in the boxes below. Then find the differences.

_____ − _____ =	_____ − _____ =	_____ − _____ =	_____ − _____ =

NAME _____ | **DATE** _____

⊞ Scout Them Out Addition D

1   Circle the strategy you are practicing today.

   Count On   Make Ten   Doubles   Doubles Plus or Minus One   Add Nine   Add Ten

2   Look at the facts below. Circle the facts you can solve using the strategy you chose.

3   Solve the circled facts first. Then solve the rest of the facts if you have time.

8	7	9	9	3	8	3
+ 7	+ 3	+ 6	+ 4	+ 8	+ 10	+ 3

10	8	1	6	5	6	6
+ 7	+ 1	+ 7	+ 7	+ 9	+ 10	+ 5

10	5	2	3	9	4	2
+ 9	+ 2	+ 7	+ 4	+ 2	+ 5	+ 8

7	8	9	5	3	4	9
+ 7	+ 3	+ 2	+ 3	+ 6	+ 6	+ 8

3	6	7	9	8	5	9
+ 9	+ 6	+ 9	+ 8	+ 8	+ 5	+ 9

4   Use the facts you circled to write four different subtraction problems in the boxes below. Then find the differences.

____ – ____ =	____ – ____ =	____ – ____ =	____ – ____ =

64

NAME _____ | DATE _____

The Tenth Century Day page 1 of 2

1 Help Cangaroo hop from 900 to 990.

- First, fill in the missing numbers along the number line.
- Then trace Cangaroo's hop to 910 and draw the rest yourself as you count by tens.

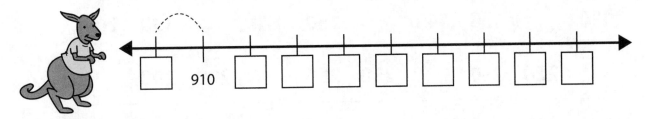

910

2 What number comes after 990 if you're counting by 10s? _____

3 When people talk about time and history, they have special names for certain numbers of years:

- 1 year: *Year*
- 10 years: *Decade*
- 100 years: *Century*
- 1,000 years: *Millennium*

Use each of these special words once in its own sentence. You can write about the past or the future. You can write statements of fact or fiction.

ex One *millennium* from today, people will be able to travel to any planet in outer space.

a

b

c

d

NAME _____ | DATE _____

The Tenth Century Day page 2 of 2

4 Here is a grid of the counting-by-ten numbers to 1,000. Fill in the missing numbers.

Hint: Use the Classroom Number Line to help.

10	20		40	50		70	80		100
110		130	140		160	170		190	200
	220	230		250	260		280	290	
310	320		340	350		370	380		400
410		430	440		460	470		490	500
	520	530		550	560		580	590	
610	620		640	650		670	680		700
710		730	740		760	770		790	800
	820	830		850	860		880	890	
910	920		940	950		970	980		1,000

5 What do you notice about the grid of numbers? Do you see any patterns? Write two observations about the grid below.

a

b

Base Ten Bank Subtraction, Sheet 1

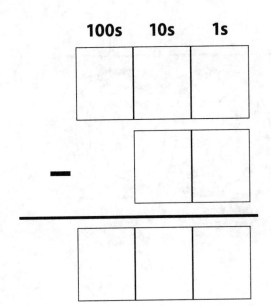

Show your work here.

Base Ten Bank Subtraction, Sheet 1

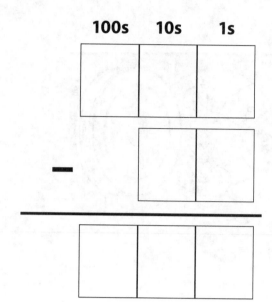

Show your work here.

Base Ten Bank Subtraction, Sheet 2

Show your work here.

Base Ten Bank Subtraction, Sheet 2

Show your work here.

NAME _____ | **DATE** _____

⊞ Scout Them Out Addition E

1 Circle the strategy or strategies you are practicing today.

Count On   Make Ten   Doubles   Doubles Plus or Minus One   Add Nine   Add Ten   Leftovers

2 Look at the facts below. Circle the facts you can solve using the strategy or strategies you chose.

3 Solve the circled facts first. Then solve the rest of the facts if you have time.

6	2	5	4	6	7	2
+ 6	+ 8	+ 9	+5	+ 3	+ 10	+ 9

3	9	10	8	6	10	9
+ 7	+ 3	+ 2	+ 8	+ 5	+ 6	+ 9

8	4	2	6	5	1	7
+ 5	+ 6	+ 7	+ 10	+ 6	+ 9	+ 8

7	4	10	6	3	10	6
+ 7	+ 7	+ 8	+ 4	+ 9	+ 9	+ 7

4	6	3	9	8	5	6
+ 4	+ 5	+ 3	+ 1	+ 4	+ 3	+ 10

5	2	6	6	10	4	2
+ 7	+ 9	+ 8	+ 10	+ 10	+ 3	+ 8

4 Use the facts you circled to write four different subtraction problems in the boxes below. Then find the differences.

_____ − _____ =	_____ − _____ =	_____ − _____ =	_____ − _____ =

71

NAME _____ |DATE _____

⊞ Scout Them Out Addition F

1   Circle the strategy or strategies you are practicing today.

Count On   Make Ten   Doubles   Doubles Plus or Minus One   Add Nine   Add Ten   Leftovers

2   Look at the facts below. Circle the facts you can solve using the strategy or strategies you chose.

3   Solve the circled facts first. Then solve the rest of the facts if you have time.

6 + 6	2 + 8	1 + 9	6 +10	6 + 3	7 + 10	2 + 9
3 + 7	9 + 3	10 + 2	4 + 4	6 + 5	3 + 3	9 + 1
8 + 5	4 + 6	2 + 7	6 + 10	5 + 6	5 + 9	7 + 8
7 + 7	4 + 7	10 + 8	6 + 4	3 + 9	10 + 9	6 + 7
4 +5	9 + 4	4 + 3	9 + 8	8 + 4	5 + 3	6 + 10
5 + 7	2 + 9	6 + 8	8 + 8	6 + 5	10 + 6	9 + 9

4   Use the facts you circled to write four different subtraction problems in the boxes below. Then find the differences.

____ − ____ =	____ − ____ =	____ − ____ =	____ − ____ =

⊞ Scout Them Out Addition G

1 Circle the strategy or strategies you are practicing today.

Count On   Make Ten   Doubles   Doubles Plus or Minus One   Add Nine   Add Ten   Leftovers

2 Look at the facts below. Circle the facts you can solve using the strategy or strategies you chose.

3 Solve the circled facts first. Then solve the rest of the facts if you have time.

7	7	6	2	4	8	8
+ 5	+ 8	+ 6	+9	+ 10	+9	+ 6

4	10	1	8	7	4	10
+ 4	+ 5	+ 9	+ 7	+ 2	+ 6	+ 8

9	4	7	6	5	6	3
+ 9	+ 5	+ 7	+ 4	+ 10	+ 7	+ 10

3	5	1	8	5	0	9
+ 7	+ 5	+ 8	+ 7	+ 9	+ 0	+ 4

5	10	3	4	7	8	5
+ 8	+ 6	+ 3	+ 5	+ 2	+ 7	+ 9

8	4	9	4	3	5	7
+ 2	+ 8	+ 1	+ 7	+ 10	+ 6	+ 8

4 Use the facts you circled to write four different subtraction problems in the boxes below. Then find the differences.

___ − ___ =	___ − ___ =	___ − ___ =	___ − ___ =

73

NAME _____ |DATE

▦ Scout Them Out Addition H

1 Circle the strategy or strategies you are practicing today.

Count On   Make Ten   Doubles   Doubles Plus or Minus One   Add Nine   Add Ten   Leftovers

2 Look at the facts below. Circle the facts you can solve using the strategy or strategies you chose.

3 Solve the circled facts first. Then solve the rest of the facts if you have time.

6 + 2	9 + 8	5 + 6	5 +8	6 + 10	9 + 4	4 + 6
3 + 4	5 + 5	10 + 7	8 + 2	9 + 5	4 + 6	10 + 10
8 + 9	4 + 3	3 + 7	6 + 8	5 + 10	6 + 9	7 + 5
7 + 7	4 + 7	10 + 8	6 + 7	1 + 9	10 + 3	9 + 7
7 + 8	6 + 4	3 + 3	9 + 5	7 + 10	8 + 4	9 + 9
8 + 3	2 + 8	9 + 1	8 + 7	3 + 10	4 + 6	8 + 8

4 Use the facts you circled to write four different subtraction problems in the boxes below. Then find the differences.

_____ – _____ =	_____ – _____ =	_____ – _____ =	_____ – _____ =

74

Put It on the Line Record Sheet 1

Game 1

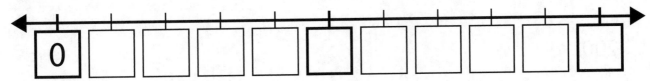

Teacher's Total	Students' Total

Game 2

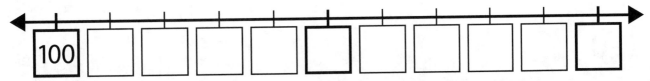

Teacher's Total	Students' Total

Put It on the Line Record Sheet 2

Game 3

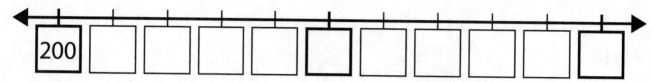

200

Teacher's Total	Students' Total

Game 4

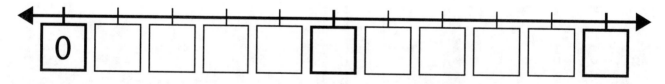

0

Teacher's Total	Students' Total

Measuring Our Plants

We planted our seeds on April _____. We planted _____ and _____.

We will use this chart to show how our plants grow this month.

	Plant 1 _____ (height in centimeters)	Amount of Change	Plant 2 _____ (height in centimeters)	Amount of Change
Date				

Plant Growth Chart

Rectangle Hunt 1

Sam used colored tiles to make a rectangle for each of the first 7 days of the month. He used 1 tile to make the rectangle for the 1st day. He used 2 tiles to make the rectangle for the 2nd day. He used 3 tiles to make the rectangle for the 3rd day, and so on. Here are four of the rectangles Sam made.

For each rectangle:

- Tell which day you think it matches.
- Cover it with tiles to find out for sure.
- Trace the tiles to show how many it took.
- Write an addition or multiplication equation to tell how many tiles it took.

I think this is the rectangle
Sam made for Day ___.

Equation:

I think this is the rectangle Sam made
for Day ___.

Equation:

I think this is the rectangle Sam made for Day ___.

Equation:

I think this is the
rectangle Sam
made for Day ___.

Equation:

◰ Rectangle Hunt 2

Sara used colored tiles to make a rectangle for the 8th through the 12th days of the month. She used 8 tiles to make the rectangle for the 8th day. She used 9 tiles to make the rectangle for the 9th day. She used 10 tiles to make the rectangle for the 10th day, and so on. Here are three of the rectangles Sara made.

For each rectangle:

- Tell which day you think it matches.
- Cover it with tiles to find out for sure.
- Trace the tiles to show how many it took.
- Write an addition or multiplication equation to tell how many tiles it took.

I think this is the rectangle Sara made for Day ___.

Equation:

I think this is the rectangle Sara made for Day ___.

Equation:

I think this is the rectangle Sara made for Day ___.

Equation:

NAME _____ |**DATE** _____

⊞ Scout Them Out Addition I

1 If you demonstrated fluency on two categories of facts and Leftovers, complete all the facts on this page.

2 If you are working on a single category or two categories of facts, circle the strategy or strategies you are practicing today.

Count On   Make Ten   Doubles   Doubles Plus or Minus One   Add Nine   Add Ten   Leftovers

3 Look at the facts below. Circle the facts you can solve using the strategies you chose.

4 Solve the circled facts first. Then solve the rest of the facts if you have time.

8 + 1	7 + 3	8 + 7	4 + 4	9 + 10	3 + 9	7 + 7
4 + 6	6 + 5	10 + 4	3 + 6	7 + 6	9 + 4	10 + 8
8 + 4	9 + 5	3 + 7	8 + 3	7 + 9	10 + 1	3 + 4
6 + 6	5 + 6	5 + 8	8 + 7	7 + 9	3 + 10	2 + 8
4 + 10	8 + 8	5 + 4	9 + 9	7 + 5	8 + 9	1 + 9
3 + 3	6 + 4	9 + 1	10 + 5	3 + 9	2 + 2	6 + 7

5 Use the facts you circled to write four different subtraction problems below. Then find the differences.

_____ − _____ =	_____ − _____ =	_____ − _____ =	_____ − _____ =

80

⊞ Scout Them Out Addition J

1 If you demonstrated fluency on two categories of facts and Leftovers, complete all the facts on this page.

2 If you are working on a single category or two categories of facts, circle the strategy or strategies you are practicing today.

Count On   Make Ten   Doubles   Doubles Plus or Minus One   Add Nine   Add Ten   Leftovers

3 Look at the facts below. Circle the facts you can solve using the strategies you chose.

4 Solve the circled facts first. Then solve the rest of the facts if you have time.

8 + 2	4 + 3	6 + 6	7 + 9	9 + 10	3 + 9	10 + 5
7 + 7	4 + 5	10 + 3	9 + 6	7 + 2	9 + 1	7 + 8
4 + 4	6 + 5	9 + 7	6 + 8	9 + 9	8 + 3	5 + 4
10 + 6	5 + 7	6 + 2	4 + 4	7 + 3	6 + 5	9 + 8
3 + 10	8 + 9	1 + 9	8 + 8	10 + 5	8 + 7	7 + 4
3 + 7	9 + 4	9 + 2	7 + 6	4 + 6	2 + 2	6 + 10

5 Use the facts you circled to write four different subtraction problems below. Then find the differences.

_____ – _____ =	_____ – _____ =	_____ – _____ =	_____ – _____ =

⊞ Scout Them Out Addition K

1 If you demonstrated fluency on two categories of facts and Leftovers, complete all the facts on this page.

2 If you are working on a single category or two categories of facts, circle the strategy or strategies you are practicing today.

Count On   Make Ten   Doubles   Doubles Plus or Minus One   Add Nine   Add Ten   Leftovers

3 Look at the facts below. Circle the facts you can solve using the strategies you chose.

4 Solve the circled facts first. Then solve the rest of the facts if you have time.

7 + 2	4 + 5	8 + 9	6 + 6	9 + 1	3 + 10	9 + 9
6 + 7	4 + 6	10 + 6	9 + 2	4 + 4	4 + 3	7 + 10
4 + 9	5 + 5	7 + 7	8 + 2	7 + 8	3 + 10	6 + 4
3 + 6	5 + 9	6 + 10	5 + 4	7 + 3	6 + 7	8 + 4
2 + 8	10 + 9	1 + 7	9 + 7	10 + 10	8 + 3	2 + 4
3 + 7	5 + 4	2 + 2	7 + 10	4 + 7	8 + 5	6 + 7

5 Use the facts you circled to write four different subtraction problems below. Then find the differences.

_____ – ____ =	_____ – ____ =	_____ – ____ =	_____ – ____ =

◻️ **Reach the Joey Record Sheet, Game 1**

It's time for Joey to come home, but he is hiding on _____.
Who will be first to find him—his mother, Flyer, or his dad, Boomer?

_30

Work Space

NAME _____ **| DATE** _____

📔 **Reach the Joey Record Sheet, Game 2**

It's time for Joey to come home, but he is hiding on _____.
Who will be first to find him—his mother, Flyer, or his dad, Boomer?

_20

Work Space

NAME | **DATE**

📅 May Hidden Picture Grid

Joey is hopping after something. Help him catch it by solving the clues on the calendar markers. Color the square to show which number Joey hops to each day. Look at the color of the day's calendar marker to know what color to use. If the day's marker is only halfway colored in, color the square on your grid exactly the same way.

10	20	30	40	50	60	70	80	90	100
110	120	130	140	150	160	170	180	190	200
210	220	230	240	250	260	270	280	290	300
310	320	330	340	350	360	370	380	390	400
410	420	430	440	450	460	470	480	490	500
510	520	530	540	550	560	570	580	590	600
610	620	630	640	650	660	670	680	690	700
710	720	730	740	750	760	770	780	790	800
810	820	830	840	850	860	870	880	890	900
910	920	930	940	950	960	970	980	990	1,000

Tens & Hundreds Picture Grid

Solve each set of problems and color in the squares as directed to make a picture of a plant you find in Australia.

Dark green:						
100 – 80	30 + 50	180 – 60	90 + 90	160 – 130	60 + 70	190 – 100
Light green:						
750 – 380	310 + 180	490 – 340	20 + 30	700 – 220	160 + 160	660 – 240
220 + 110	190 – 130	160 + 220	60 + 220			
Gray:						
190 + 170	30 + 110	880 – 230	130 + 120	580 + 170	530 – 370	870 – 410	220 + 340
400 – 170	740 – 190	940 – 180	490 – 220	300 + 360	680 – 340	210 + 240
Brown:						
950 – 70	450 + 450	370 + 450	570 + 290	1,000 – 160		

10	20	30	40	50	60	70	80	90	100
110	120	130	140	150	160	170	180	190	200
210	220	230	240	250	260	270	280	290	300
310	320	330	340	350	360	370	380	390	400
410	420	430	440	450	460	470	480	490	500
510	520	530	540	550	560	570	580	590	600
610	620	630	640	650	660	670	680	690	700
710	720	730	740	750	760	770	780	790	800
810	820	830	840	850	860	870	880	890	900
910	920	930	940	950	960	970	980	990	1,000

Unknowns Picture Grid 1

Solve each set of problems and color in the squares as directed to make a picture of an animal you find in Australia.

Orange:		
$100 - \boxed{} = 90$ (color in the bottom-right half)	$10 + \boxed{} = 30$	$20 + \boxed{} = 50$ (color in the bottom-left half)

Yellow:

$60 + \boxed{} = 190$ $\qquad$ $70 + \boxed{} = 180$ $\qquad$ $80 + \boxed{} = 200$

Black:

$890 - \boxed{} = 220$ $\qquad$ $680 - \boxed{} = 230$ $\qquad$ $1,000 - \boxed{} = 110$ $\qquad$ $430 - \boxed{} = 200$

Green:

$\boxed{} - 320 = 460$ $\qquad$ $160 + \boxed{} = 490$ $\qquad$ $150 + \boxed{} = 500$ $\qquad$ $290 + \boxed{} = 850$

$770 - \boxed{} = 200$ $\qquad$ $930 - \boxed{} = 380$ $\qquad$ $\boxed{} + 130 = 900$ $\qquad$ $\boxed{} + 60 = 850$

$\boxed{} - 290 = 700$ $\qquad$ $\boxed{} - 290 = 710$ $\qquad$ $710 - \boxed{} = 370$

10	20	30	40	50	60	70	80	90	100
110	120	130	140	150	160	170	180	190	200
210	220	230	240	250	260	270	280	290	300
310	320	330	340	350	360	370	380	390	400
410	420	430	440	450	460	470	480	490	500
510	520	530	540	550	560	570	580	590	600
610	620	630	640	650	660	670	680	690	700
710	720	730	740	750	760	770	780	790	800
810	820	830	840	850	860	870	880	890	900
910	920	930	940	950	960	970	980	990	1,000

Unknowns Picture Grid 2

Solve each set of problems and color in the squares as directed to make a picture of something people used to wear in Australia to keep the flies away.

Green:

$\boxed{} = 940 - 170$ $870 = \boxed{} + 240$ $240 = 970 - \boxed{}$ $980 = 300 + \boxed{}$

$820 = \boxed{} + 70$ $160 = 950 - \boxed{}$ $\boxed{} = 960 - 270$ $900 = 140 + \boxed{}$

$\boxed{} = 250 + 370$ $380 = \boxed{} - 340$ $1{,}000 = \boxed{} + 20$ $\boxed{} = 180 + 560$

Choose and use 3 different colors, none of them green:

$930 - 360 = \boxed{}$ $180 + \boxed{} = 620$ $970 - \boxed{} = 50$ $170 + 370 = \boxed{}$

$800 - 350 = \boxed{}$ $\boxed{} + 230 = 570$ $930 - \boxed{} = 370$ $220 + 440 = \boxed{}$

$130 + 230 = \boxed{}$ $\boxed{} + 160 = 830$ $\boxed{} + 540 = 1{,}000$ $\boxed{} + 140 = 780$

$\boxed{} + 20 = 1{,}000$ $\boxed{} + 340 = 890$ $520 - \boxed{} = 170$ $\boxed{} - 320 = 50$

$730 - \boxed{} = 260$ $1{,}000 - 50 = \boxed{}$ $690 - \boxed{} = 40$

10	20	30	40	50	60	70	80	90	100
110	120	130	140	150	160	170	180	190	200
210	220	230	240	250	260	270	280	290	300
310	320	330	340	350	360	370	380	390	400
410	420	430	440	450	460	470	480	490	500
510	520	530	540	550	560	570	580	590	600
610	620	630	640	650	660	670	680	690	700
710	720	730	740	750	760	770	780	790	800
810	820	830	840	850	860	870	880	890	900
910	920	930	940	950	960	970	980	990	1,000

NAME _____ | **DATE** _____

Line Plot Form

This month, we are going to collect height data. We are going to measure the height of every second grader in our class, and then the height of every kindergartener in one class and the height of every fifth grader in another class. Here are my predictions about how things will turn out when we measure and compare the heights of kids in these three different age groups:

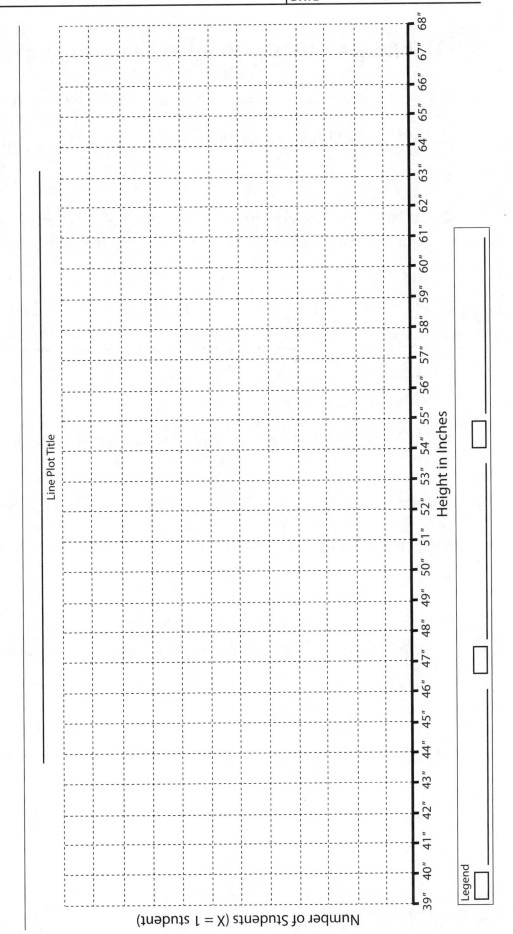

Line Plot Title

Number of Students (X = 1 student)

39" 40" 41" 42" 43" 44" 45" 46" 47" 48" 49" 50" 51" 52" 53" 54" 55" 56" 57" 58" 59" 60" 61" 62" 63" 64" 65" 66" 67" 68"

Height in Inches

Legend

Thinking About the Height Data page 1 of 2

1 Answer these questions about the second grade height data you collected today.

   a What is the height of the shortest second grader? _____ inches

   b What is the height of the tallest second grader? _____ inches

   c What is the difference between the height of the shortest and the tallest second grader? Show your work. (Use the open number line to help if you like.)

   Answer: _____ inches

   d What is the most common height for the second graders? _____ inches

2 Answer these questions about the kindergarten height data you collected today.

   a What is the height of the shortest kindergartner? _____ inches

   b What is the height of the tallest kindergartner? _____ inches

   c What is the difference between the height of the shortest and the tallest kindergartner? Show your work. (Use the open number line to help if you like.)

   Answer: _____ inches

   d What is the most common height for the kindergartners? _____ inches

(continued on next page)

Thinking About the Height Data page 2 of 2

3 Answer these questions about the fifth grade height data you collected today.

a What is the height of the shortest fifth grader? _____ inches

b What is the height of the tallest fifth grader? _____ inches

c What is the difference between the height of the shortest and the tallest fifth grader? Show your work. (Use the open number line to help if you like.)

Answer: _____ inches

d What is the most common height for the fifth graders? _____ inches

4 Put the most common height for each grade level in order from least to most on the lines below. Use the information to answer questions a, b, and c.

Note If there are 2 or more most common heights for a grade level, use the greatest.

_____ inches   _____ inches   _____ inches

When you use the most common height for each grade level,

a How much taller is a second grader than a kindergartner? _____ inches

b How much taller is a fifth grader than a kindergartner? _____ inches

c How much taller is a fifth grader than a second grader? _____ inches

5 Describe one thing that was interesting or surprising to you about the data your class collected this month.

NAME _____ | **DATE** _____

▨ Rectangle Review page 1 of 2

Number of Tiles	Dimensions of Rectangle	Equations to Match Rectangle
1		
2		
3		
4		
4		
5		
6		
6		
7		
8		
8		
9		
9		
10		
10		
11		
12		
12		
12		
13		
14		
14		
15		
15		
16		
16		
16		
17		
18		

(continued on next page)

92

Rectangle Review page 2 of 2

Number of Tiles	Dimensions of Rectangle	Equations to Match Rectangle
18		
18		
19		
20		
20		
20		
21		
21		
22		
22		
23		
24		
24		
24		
24		
25		
25		
26		
26		
27		
27		
28		
28		
29		
30		
30		
30		
30		
31		

NAME _____ | DATE _____

⊞ Scout Them Out Addition L

1 If you demonstrated fluency on two categories of facts and Leftovers, complete all the facts on this page.

2 If you are working on a single category or two categories of facts, circle the strategy or strategies you are practicing today.

Count On   Make Ten   Doubles   Doubles Plus or Minus One   Add Nine   Add Ten   Leftovers

3 Look at the facts below. Circle the facts you can solve using the strategies you chose.

4 Solve the circled facts first. Then solve the rest of the facts if you have time.

8	5	7	6	9	5	9
+ 3	+ 5	+ 6	+6	+ 4	+ 10	+2

4	5	10	7	8	6	7
+ 8	+ 4	+ 9	+ 3	+ 8	+ 10	+ 8

9	5	3	8	7	4	3
+ 9	+ 6	+ 7	+ 1	+ 7	+ 6	+ 10

3	8	6	10	1	6	7
+ 3	+ 9	+ 5	+ 4	+ 9	+ 6	+ 8

2	9	7	6	10	9	5
+ 5	+ 1	+ 5	+ 2	+ 0	+ 3	+ 8

4	5	8	7	1	4	7
+ 4	+ 10	+ 2	+ 9	+ 1	+ 10	+ 7

5 Use the facts you circled to write four different subtraction problems below. Then find the differences.

____ – ____ =	____ – ____ =	____ – ____ =	____ – ____ =

⊞ Scout Them Out Addition M

1 If you demonstrated fluency on two categories of facts and Leftovers, complete all the facts on this page.

2 If you are working on a single category or two categories of facts, circle the strategy or strategies you are practicing today.

Count On   Make Ten   Doubles   Doubles Plus or Minus One   Add Nine   Add Ten   Leftovers

3 Look at the facts below. Circle the facts you can solve using the strategies you chose.

4 Solve the circled facts first. Then solve the rest of the facts if you have time.

3 + 3	6 + 5	7 + 9	10 + 6	6 + 4	7 + 2	9 + 3
6 + 7	5 + 5	10 + 6	7 + 4	9 + 8	3 + 10	7 + 3
9 + 8	6 + 6	3 + 10	8 + 8	10 + 7	5 + 6	3 + 7
9 + 3	8 + 2	10 + 5	4 + 4	5 + 9	6 + 7	7 + 2
5 + 8	9 + 4	9 + 9	3 + 7	10 + 8	9 + 8	2 + 6
7 + 4	5 + 6	3 + 2	4 + 6	5 + 5	4 + 9	10 + 7

5 Use the facts you circled to write four different subtraction problems below. Then find the differences.

_____ – _____ =	_____ – _____ =	_____ – _____ =	_____ – _____ =

⊞ Scout Them Out Addition N

1 If you demonstrated fluency on two categories of facts and Leftovers, complete all the facts on this page.

2 If you are working on a single category or two categories of facts, circle the strategy or strategies you are practicing today.

Count On   Make Ten   Doubles   Doubles Plus or Minus One   Add Nine   Add Ten   Leftovers

3 Look at the facts below. Circle the facts you can solve using the strategies you chose.

4 Solve the circled facts first. Then solve the rest of the facts if you have time.

3 + 4	6 + 6	1 + 9	7 + 6	6 + 10	9 + 2	5 + 3
3 + 7	5 + 9	10 + 8	2 + 7	9 + 9	6 + 10	7 + 6
9 + 7	10 + 6	2 + 8	6 + 8	7 + 7	5 + 9	3 + 4
3 + 3	10 + 2	10 + 9	4 + 4	9 + 1	6 + 5	7 + 3
8 + 8	4 + 10	9 + 6	5 + 8	7 + 8	9 + 3	2 + 2
10 + 10	5 + 3	8 + 2	7 + 4	5 + 10	1 + 9	10 + 9

5 Use the facts you circled to write four different subtraction problems below. Then find the differences.

_____ – _____ =	_____ – _____ =	_____ – _____ =	_____ – _____ =

96

Number Neighbors

Look at the number in the center square. Find this number's neighbors and write these numbers in the squares around the number. Check your answers on the thousands grid.

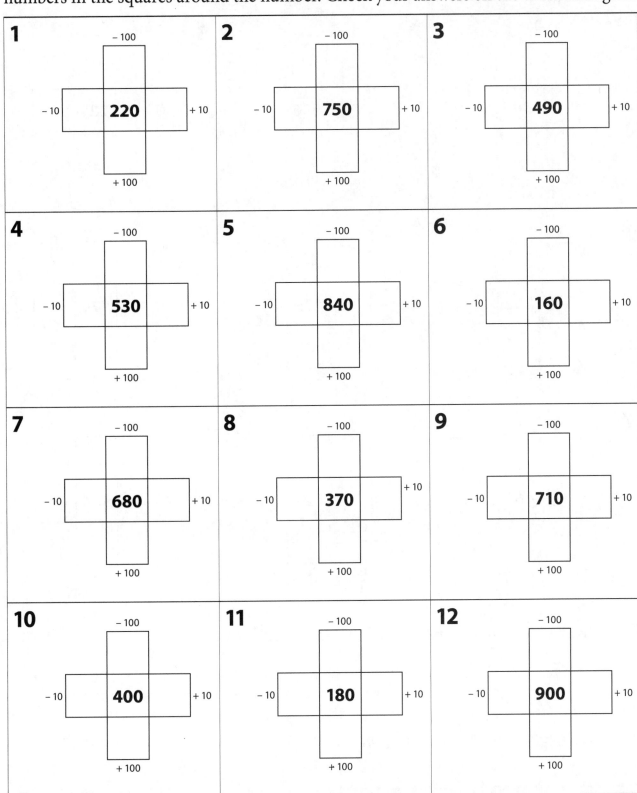

1
− 100

− 10 **220** + 10

+ 100

2
− 100

− 10 **750** + 10

+ 100

3
− 100

− 10 **490** + 10

+ 100

4
− 100

− 10 **530** + 10

+ 100

5
− 100

− 10 **840** + 10

+ 100

6
− 100

− 10 **160** + 10

+ 100

7
− 100

− 10 **680** + 10

+ 100

8
− 100

− 10 **370** + 10

+ 100

9
− 100

− 10 **710** + 10

+ 100

10
− 100

− 10 **400** + 10

+ 100

11
− 100

− 10 **180** + 10

+ 100

12
− 100

− 10 **900** + 10

+ 100

NAME _____ | **DATE** _____

📦 More Number Neighbors

Look at the number in the center square. Add and subtract 10 and 100 to this number to find its neighbors. Write these numbers in the squares around the number.

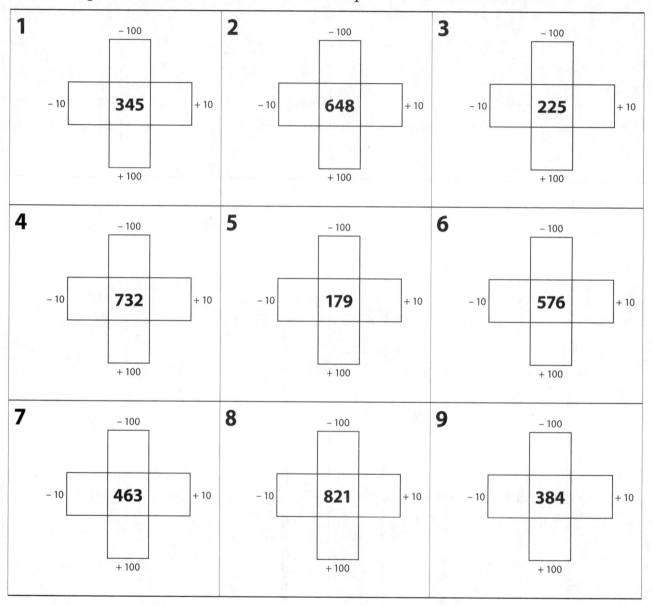

1
– 100
– 10 **345** + 10
+ 100

2
– 100
– 10 **648** + 10
+ 100

3
– 100
– 10 **225** + 10
+ 100

4
– 100
– 10 **732** + 10
+ 100

5
– 100
– 10 **179** + 10
+ 100

6
– 100
– 10 **576** + 10
+ 100

7
– 100
– 10 **463** + 10
+ 100

8
– 100
– 10 **821** + 10
+ 100

9
– 100
– 10 **384** + 10
+ 100

10 What happens to the tens digit when you add 10 to a number?

_____

11 What happens to the hundreds digit when you subtract 100 from a number?

_____

Race Up to One Thousand Record Sheet

Game 1

We are playing for _____. Our starting number is _____.

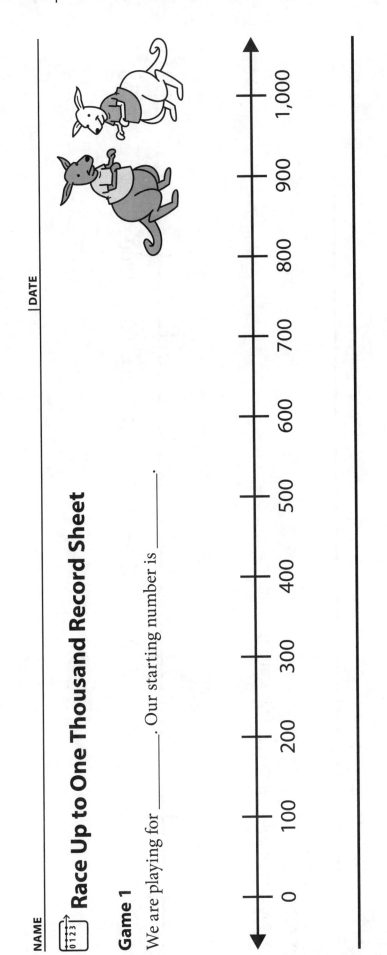

0 100 200 300 400 500 600 700 800 900 1,000

Game 2

We are playing for _____. Our starting number is _____.

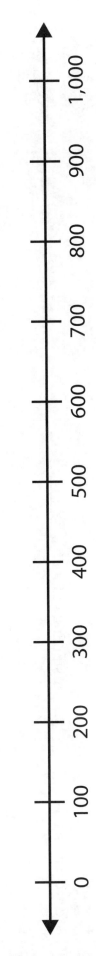

0 100 200 300 400 500 600 700 800 900 1,000

NAME

DATE

Race Back to Zero Record Sheet

Game 1

We are playing for _____. Our starting number is _____.

0   100   200   300   400   500   600   700   800   900   1,000

Game 2

We are playing for _____. Our starting number is _____.

0   100   200   300   400   500   600   700   800   900   1,000

100